INDIANS

POCAHONTAS, *Seymour*
SACAGAWEA, *Seymour*
SITTING BULL, *Stevenson*
TECUMSEH, *Stevenson*

NAVAL HEROES

DAVID FARRAGUT, *Long*
GEORGE DEWEY, *Long*
JOHN PAUL JONES, *Snow*
MATTHEW CALBRAITH PERRY, *Scharbach*
OLIVER HAZARD PERRY, *Long*
RAPHAEL SEMMES, *Snow*
STEPHEN DECATUR, *Smith*

NOTED WIVES and MOTHERS

ABIGAIL ADAMS, *Wagoner*
DOLLY MADISON, *Monsell*
JESSIE FREMONT, *Wagoner*
MARTHA WASHINGTON, *Wagoner*
MARY TODD LINCOLN, *Wilkie*
NANCY HANKS, *Stevenson*
RACHEL JACKSON, *Govan*

SCIENTISTS and INVENTORS

ALECK BELL, *Widdemer*
ELI WHITNEY, *Snow*
GEORGE CARVER, *Stevenson*
GEORGE EASTMAN, *Henry*
HENRY FORD, *Aird-Ruddiman*
JOHN AUDUBON, *Mason*
LUTHER BURBANK, *Burt*
MARIA MITCHELL, *Melin*
ROBERT FULTON, *Henry*
SAMUEL MORSE, *Snow*
TOM EDISON, *Guthridge*
WALTER REED, *Higgins*
WILBUR AND ORVILLE WRIGHT, *Stevenson*
WILL AND CHARLIE MAYO, *Hammontree*

SOCIAL LEADERS

BETSY ROSS, *Weil*
BOOKER T. WASHINGTON, *Stevenson*
CLARA BARTON, *Stevenson*
DAN BEARD, *Mason*
JANE ADDAMS, *Wagoner*
JULIA WARD HOWE, *Wagoner*
JULIETTE LOW, *Higgins*
LUCRETIA MOTT, *Burnett*
MOLLY PITCHER, *Stevenson*
SUSAN ANTHONY, *Monsell*

SOLDIERS

ANTHONY WAYNE, *Stevenson*
BEDFORD FORREST, *Parks*
DAN MORGAN, *Bryant*
ETHAN ALLAN, *Winders*
FRANCIS MARION, *Steele*
ISRAEL PUTNAM, *Stevenson*
JEB STUART, *Winders*
NATHANAEL GREENE, *Peckham*
ROBERT E. LEE, *Monsell*
TOM JACKSON, *Monsell*
U. S. GRANT, *Stevenson*
WILLIAM HENRY HARRISON, *Peckham*
ZACK TAYLOR, *Wilkie*

STATESMEN

ABE LINCOLN, *Stevenson*
ANDY JACKSON, *Stevenson*
DAN WEBSTER, *Smith*
FRANKLIN ROOSEVELT, *Weil*
HENRY CLAY, *Monsell*
JAMES MONROE, *Widdemer*
JOHN MARSHALL, *Monsell*
SAM HOUSTON, *Stevenson*
TEDDY ROOSEVELT, *Parks*
WOODROW WILSON, *Monsell*

Sequoyah

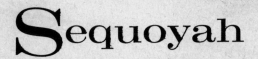

Young Cherokee Guide

Presented to
Allan Williams
by
The Parent-Teachers Association
Winner of The First Prize
in
The Library Contest
in
Mrs. Hobart's Third Grade
at
West School 1961-62

Mrs. Ellen Mello
and
Mrs. Dorothy Manning
Librarians

Illustrated by Frank Giacoia

alan Williams

Hingham - Massachusetts

Sequoyah

Young Cherokee Guide

By Dorothea J. Snow

THE **BOBBS-MERRILL** COMPANY, INC.
A SUBSIDIARY OF HOWARD W. SAMS & CO., INC.
Publishers · INDIANAPOLIS · NEW YORK

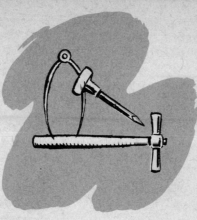

To Elizabeth Parks Beamguard,
always ready with a word of
encouragement

Illustrations

Full Pages

Numerous smaller illustrations

Contents

 ★ ★ ★

Books by Dorothea J. Snow

ELI WHITNEY: BOY MECHANIC

JOHN PAUL JONES: SALT-WATER BOY

RAPHAEL SEMMES: TIDEWATER BOY

SAMUEL MORSE: INQUISITIVE BOY

SEQUOYAH: YOUNG CHEROKEE GUIDE

Sequoyah

Young Cherokee Guide

All Cherokee

"SEE Sikwayi," teased Ta-yau-i-ta, or Young Beaver, calling from behind a tree in the woods. "See Sikwayi dig the ground and plant seeds! He does squaw work!"

Sikwayi did not look up. With his hoe, made from a shell tied to the end of a stick, he kept on digging holes in the garden patch. Into each hole he dropped two seeds of corn and covered them. One seed was for the crows and the other for his mother, Wur-teh, and himself.

"Sikwayi, the little squaw!" Now I-na-li, or Black Fox, took up the teasing. "He cannot hit the target with his arrow, but he can dig holes in the ground and plant seeds. Sikwayi does squaw work!"

Without answering, Sikwayi went on with his task. Wur-teh had said that the corn should be planted today, and he wanted to be sure to finish planting it.

It was an early spring morning in 1775. The sun shone warmly on the garden and log cabin on the hillside. Not far away was the Cherokee village of Taskigi. On all sides rose the mist-covered mountains which the Cherokees called the Great Smokies.

Soon A-wa-ni-ta, Young Deer, began teasing. "Sikwayi cannot win a race," he said, "but he can bring in wood for a fire! Squaw work!"

Sikwayi reached the end of the row. He straightened up. His face looked calm. He must never let his face show how he felt inside.

He wished he were like the other boys of the village. He wished he could run and play games and shoot his bow and arrow all the time. But he couldn't. For one thing, he must help his mother. Wur-teh could not do the work of her absent husband and her own, too. For another thing, Sikwayi was lame and could not get about as easily as the other boys could.

Young Beaver, Black Fox, and Young Deer stepped out of the woods. Another boy, Lone Bear, was with them. He lived in the near-by village of Towsee and often came to Wur-teh's store with his grandfather. His grandfather was Wur-teh's uncle.

"Will Sikwayi come this evening to shoot with us?" Young Deer asked. "And miss the target?"

"Or throw his pole over the hoop instead of through it?" asked Black Fox.

Sikwayi looked the boys straight in the eyes. "I will come," he said softly. He smiled, for he knew their teasing was all in fun. "Some day I shall win at something."

"That will be the day the morning fails to come!" Young Deer said with a laugh.

Winning their games and races meant a great deal to all young Cherokee boys. The training they received from these games and races made them strong, they believed. It also helped to make them great hunters and brave warriors like their fathers. All Cherokee boys wanted to be known as great hunters and warriors.

Young Beaver and Young Deer and Black Fox pointed to the small basket Sikwayi carried. It was still half full of corn seed.

"Planting corn is squaw work!" they cried and ran back toward the village.

"It is his white blood that makes him do such things," Young Beaver said. "All white men do squaw work in the fields."

Lone Bear turned and gave Sikwayi a comforting look. He knew how Sikwayi felt. He was half white, too!

14

Clop, clop. Sikwayi heard the sound of horses' hoofs on the trail to the cabin. He lifted his head from his planting. He saw the packhorse coming out of the forest.

He saw another horse, with a man riding it, following the packhorse. Joy and hope welled up in the boy. Perhaps his father was coming back home!

Sikwayi knew very little about his father, Nathaniel Gist. Gist had been a trader. On a trip through the Cherokee country he had married Wur-teh, the daughter of a chief of the Red Paint clan. Sikwayi had never seen him.

"Your father will return," Wur-teh often said. "He said he would when he went away."

All traders were white men. If the man coming up the trail was his father, Sikwayi knew it would make Wur-teh happy. It would make Sikwayi happy, too. His father could take care of the trading post. His mother could do her work. And Sikwayi could shoot and play games with the other boys. He would become as skillful as they.

Sikwayi drew a happy breath. He dropped his shell hoe and ran limping to the cabin. The man with the pack drew nearer.

Sikwayi saw a sad look come into his mother's eyes. He knew the short, fat man sliding from the saddle was not his father.

The man looked at Sikwayi and his mother with friendly blue eyes. He held his arm across his chest and pointed one finger skyward. He folded his arms and pointed two fingers skyward. Then he swept his right hand outward.

In the sign language which all Indians used, this meant "Good morning."

Wur-teh and Sikwayi made the same sign.

The man smiled, raised two fingers, then crossed his hands. This sign meant "Trade."

17

Wur-teh nodded, pleased. She could not speak the white man's language, and the white man could not speak Cherokee. Still, they could communicate with each other. The Indians spoke many languages, but their sign language was the same everywhere.

The trader took the packs from his horse. He opened them and laid his wares on the ground. There were knives, scissors, needles, and axes. There were also pans, kettles, calico cloth, and colored beads.

Wur-teh chose things she thought her people would buy. The trader laid them aside.

Sikwayi pointed to some tiny polished bells. Wur-teh took a dozen of them. The Cherokees liked to fasten these bells to their moccasins or sleeves or skirts. The bells made a pleasant tinkling sound when one walked.

Wur-teh brought out several bundles of furs which she had got in trade from her people. The trader looked the furs over. He nodded and made the sign for "Fine."

The trading was over. Everyone was pleased.

The trader packed quickly. Then, just as he mounted his horse, he drew something from his saddlebag. It was round and red. With a small knife he cut off a piece and ate it.

He saw the wondering eyes of Wur-teh and her son. Grinning, he cut off two pieces and gave one to each of them.

"Apple," he said. There was no sign for that word in sign language.

Wur-teh and Sikwayi put the pieces in their mouths and chewed. Looks of delight spread over their faces.

Wur-teh made the sign for "Good."

The man nodded and left.

The taste of the apple lingered. It was a kind of fruit Wur-teh and Sikwayi had never seen before. They had eaten all kinds of berries and wild plums and persimmons. But the white man's apple was better than any fruit they had ever eaten.

Wur-teh and Sikwayi gathered up the things they had bought and took them into the cabin. Wur-teh put them on shelves laid on pegs stuck in the log walls.

Wur-teh looked at her son lovingly. "He will come," she said quietly. "Some day your father will come."

THE MATCH

Later that afternoon, Sikwayi made his way alone to a clearing outside the village.

Young Beaver, Black Fox, Young Deer, and several other boys were there. The grandfather of each boy was there, too. The old men sat together in the shade of an oak tree. They were watching the boys play a game of hoop and pole.

"It is your turn, Black Fox," said the grandfather of Young Beaver.

Black Fox stepped up. In his hand was a long, straight stick.

Young Beaver held the hoop. It was made of stiff braided grass.

"Now," said the grandfather of Young Beaver.

Young Beaver rolled the hoop several feet in front of Black Fox. Black Fox aimed his stick and threw it. The stick went cleanly through the rolling hoop.

"See! See!" cried the old men. They turned toward the grandfather of Black Fox.

"You have taught your grandson well."

The grandfather of Black Fox beamed. For a grandfather there could be no greater praise.

Every afternoon, in good weather, the boys and their grandfathers gathered here. The boys raced. They wrestled and held shooting matches. They played games. The old men taught their

grandsons all the skills they themselves had
known as young men. In the land of the Cherokee that was the job of men who were too old
to hunt or fight.

Wur-teh's father had died when Sikwayi was
a baby. Having no grandfather, Sikwayi had to
learn by watching others.

It came Sikwayi's turn to throw the pole. He
tried hard. But he could not throw it through
the rolling hoop. He needed practice, but there
was no one to roll the hoop for him.

Then came the race. Sikwayi did not take part in that. He could not run fast enough to beat even the slowest of the other boys.

"We will have a shooting match," said the grandfather of Young Deer.

Sikwayi hurried to get his bow and arrows. He had made them himself. They were well made, but not so well made as those of the other boys. The other boys' grandfathers had helped them.

"He who shoots his arrow closest to the center of the target wins all the arrows stuck there," said the grandfather of Young Beaver.

One by one the boys stood the right distance from the target. Each boy carefully raised his bow, aimed, and let the arrow go. Each boy's arrow had a stripe of a different color painted around it. It was easy to tell to whom the arrows belonged.

A murmur went up as Loud Thunder's arrow hit the target exactly in the center.

"Now it is your turn, Sikwayi," said the grandfather of Young Beaver.

Everyone watched closely.

Sikwayi trembled inside. He placed his arrow carefully in the bow. He raised the bow and pulled back the string. He aimed and released the arrow.

Twang! The arrow missed the target completely and disappeared in the bushes beyond!

"Do not feel bad, Sikwayi," Loud Thunder said in a half-mocking voice. "One must be *all* Indian to be good at Indian games."

Sikwayi said nothing. But he felt sad as he walked homeward. He had not won a single match. Then he lifted his head. A look of determination came over his face. He would keep on trying. Some day he would show the others that, even though he did have white blood, he was *all* Cherokee!

White Man's Wesa

"From the wood of the great ash tree
   I make a bowl,
   A bowl to eat from,
   A bowl for my mother to eat from . . ."

SIKWAYI sang his "Song to Whittle By." He made
up the words as he went along. He had made up
many such songs, work songs and play songs.
Sometimes he sang the songs Wur-teh had
taught him. But he liked his own songs best.

With a knife from his mother's trading post,
Sikwayi was whittling a bowl. He had selected
the wood for the bowl with great care. From
the pieces he cut for the fireplace he always

saved those which he thought would be best for whittling.

Some of his bowls and spoons Sikwayi had sold in the trading post. This pleased him. A Cherokee craftsman took pride in his work.

Sikwayi was whittling and singing and thinking of the piece of wonderful fruit the trader had given him. He could still taste it.

He and Wur-teh had talked about it after the trader left.

"Your father told me of such a fruit," Wur-teh had said. "It grows on trees."

"I wish we had such a tree," Sikwayi had said.

If he had some seeds of the fruit he could plant them. The Cherokees were good farmers. Sikwayi was sure if he had some apple seeds he could grow apple trees.

He was so lost in work and thought that he did not hear Lone Bear and Lone Bear's grandfather, Running Wolf, enter the cabin.

"I am in need of an ax," Running Wolf said softly. "Would the son of Wur-teh trade one for a fine beaver pelt?"

Sikwayi jumped. The words of his song stopped. He felt sheepish.

"I am sorry, Uncle," he said. "I did not hear you. We have some fine axes."

He led Lone Bear and Running Wolf over to the axes. The old man was really Wur-teh's uncle, but Sikwayi called him uncle, too. He had married into the Wolf clan and lived in the nearby village of Towsee. When a Cherokee man married he went to live in the village of his wife. Children were born into the clans of their mothers. Lone Bear belonged to the Wolf Clan, too. His father was a white trapper who lived in Towsee.

Running Wolf and Lone Bear turned to leave. Black Fox and his grandfather came in. The men greeted each other. So did the boys.

The grandfather of Black Fox turned to Running Wolf. "A white man has built a cabin on Am-a-da-hi," he said. "He has brought with him his wife and two children."

"Will the chiefs of the villages let him stay?" asked Running Wolf.

The grandfather of Black Fox shrugged. "There is enough land for all," he said.

"That is true," said Running Wolf. He and Lone Bear left with the ax.

Black Fox and his grandfather bought a large handful of beads.

"My mother is making new moccasins for me," Black Fox said proudly.

The old man handed Sikwayi one of the white man's round pieces of silver. Sikwayi did not know how much the coin was worth. But he took it in exchange for the beads. Wur-teh had five other silver coins.

The grandfather of Black Fox stopped in the

doorway. "I hope the white man did not bring a wesa with him," he said.

At that moment Wur-teh entered the cabin. "I hope so, too," she said. "It is an evil creature, the white man's wesa."

Sikwayi said nothing. He was not worrying about a wesa. He was wondering whether the white man had brought apple seeds to plant.

THINKING PLACE

For three days Sikwayi wondered about the new settler and apple seeds. Then Lone Bear came by.

"Let us go hunting," Lone Bear said. "My mother would like some bright feathers. She is putting them in a design for a new blanket. Perhaps we can shoot an oriole or some other bird with beautiful feathers."

Wur-teh heard Lone Bear. She nodded to her

son. "Go with your cousin," she said. "I can take care of things for a while."

Sikwayi was pleased. He liked to roam in the woods, hunting or fishing, and did so whenever he had a chance.

With blowguns in hand, the boys started out.

"I shot a woodpecker yesterday," Lone Bear boasted. "I got some pretty feathers from it."

Sikwayi looked at his cousin admiringly. To hit a small bird with a dart from a blowgun took a great deal of skill.

The blowguns were made from straight reeds or pieces of cane. The boys dropped hot coals through the reeds to hollow them out. A blowgun made a fine weapon for hunting birds and small game.

Not far from the cabin Sikwayi stopped and pointed to a small hut made of brush. It nestled in the shade of tall trees close to a brook.

"This is my thinking place," he said. He went

stream. As they walked along through the forest Lone Bear shot a bluebird.

"These feathers will look fine on Mother's blanket," he said.

Sikwayi wasn't listening.

"There it is!" he cried suddenly. He pointed to a log cabin in a small stump-filled clearing.

The white man's home was exactly like the cabins built by the Cherokees. It had one room. At one end was a chimney made of woven willow branches thickly covered with mud.

Most of the clearing was behind the cabin. A white man and woman were hoeing the ground between the stumps.

The boys crept toward the cabin. They were not afraid of the people. But suppose the family had brought——

Then they saw it! A wesa! It was sitting on the stone step before the cabin door, slicking down its fur with its tongue.

"Run!" cried Lone Bear. "Don't let it cross your path! It is bad magic!" He turned and fled.

Sikwayi stood still. He was afraid, too, but if he ran away, how could he get any apple seeds?

GOOD TRADE

Sikwayi had never seen a wesa before. As he stood watching it, it left the stone step.

"Meow!" it said. Its slanting yellow eyes were on Sikwayi. It came toward him.

Sikwayi began to tremble a little. When the wesa reached him, it rubbed against his bare leg. Sikwayi shivered. But the animal made no move to harm him, so he stood still.

From a distance, Lone Bear watched, wide-eyed. His father was a white man, too, but his white blood did not give him the courage to face a wesa!

Then the white man and his wife came around

34

to the front of the cabin. With them was a boy about Sikwayi's age.

"Howdy," said the white man in a friendly voice. "I see you've made friends with our cat."

Sikwayi made the sign for "Good morning."

The white man looked puzzled. He did not know the Indians' sign language.

Sikwayi was puzzled, too. If he could not talk to the man, how could he ask him about the apple seeds?

Suddenly he picked up a stick and drew a picture of an apple in the dirt. He drew a picture of a tree. Then he drew several seeds.

From the pouch on a string around his waist he took the piece of white man's silver. He held it out in his hand.

The white man still looked puzzled.

The white boy looked at the pictures on the ground. "An apple!" he cried. "Papa, he drew a picture of an apple!"

"And an apple tree!" said the woman.

The man looked again. "And apple seeds. He wants to trade the coin for apple seeds."

The woman laughed. She went into the cabin and returned with a small leather bag. Opening the bag, she held it out so that Sikwayi could look inside it.

The bag was full of apple seeds! Sikwayi felt good. He had made the white people understand. They could read his picture language.

The woman poured some of the seeds into Sikwayi's pouch. Sikwayi handed her the silver coin. The trade was made.

Then the white boy drew something in the dirt. Sikwayi looked at the picture. The boy had drawn several sun rays above the tree. He had drawn several apples on the tree.

Sikwayi grinned at the white boy. The boy was hoping that the seeds would grow into trees and bear fruit. A warm spot for his father's people grew in Sikwayi's heart. They were good people, almost as good as the Cherokees.

Sikwayi ran back to where Lone Bear was standing. He gave Lone Bear several of the seeds. Together they went back to Wur-teh's trading post.

"You have made a good trade," Wur-teh said. "We shall plant the seeds. Someday we shall have apple trees."

"And all the apples we can eat!" Sikwayi smacked his lips.

Lone Bear shook his head in wonder. "I could never have done it," he said. "I'm not afraid of many things, but I could never have stood there and let that wesa rub against my legs. Weren't you afraid?"

"Of course I was afraid," Sikwayi answered with a laugh. "But I've eaten an apple and you never have!"

Bright Hope

I⊤ ᴡᴀꜱ early one spring morning, several years later. Mist rose from the valleys and wreathed the tops of the mountains. Flowering shrubs were blooming everywhere.

Sikwayi and Wur-teh stood admiring their new springhouse. Sikwayi had built it over the brook that flowed behind the cabin. He had seen a springhouse like it at the white man's place. On shelves inside sat pails of sweet milk and butter-milk. Near by were a mound of butter and a basket of eggs. The cool moist air kept every-thing in the springhouse sweet and fresh.

Sikwayi and his mother owned a cow now, as

38

several of the Cherokee people did. Wur-teh had bought it from the white man, Mr. Thompson, for several silver coins.

Happiness bubbled over in Sikwayi as he looked from the springhouse to the small orchard in the clearing beyond. His young apple trees were blooming beautifully.

"How long we have waited for this day!" he cried happily.

Wur-teh smiled. "How hard you have worked for it!" she said.

Wur-teh was proud of her son. He was taller now and more handsome. There was a dark, thoughtful look in his eyes. His gentle nature showed in every word and deed.

Sikwayi tried hard to be like the other Indian boys his age. But he was different. The springhouse showed that. No other boy in Taskigi had thought to build one for his mother.

In some ways Sikwayi was like his father's

people. In some ways he was like his mother's. To Wur-teh he seemed to be a blend of the best of both of them.

He could not keep up with the other boys in a race or in a ball game. But he could shoot and hunt as well as anyone now. He had tried harder than any of the other boys. Yet he still worked in the garden and helped in the trading post. And he was always making something or other with his hands.

"Your father will be pleased with such a son," Wur-teh often said. And she always added, "When he comes back."

Sikwayi had worked hard on the orchard. He had planted the apple seeds. When there had been no rain to water them, he had carried water to them from the creek.

Some of the seedlings he had given to others in the village. Now these trees were in bloom, too. Lone Bear's seeds had not come up. He had let his sister plant them and had failed to water them. Sikwayi had given him some seedlings to transplant.

Today the future looked bright for Sikwayi and his mother. There would be apples in the fall. There would be pumpkins, squash, beans, and many other good things to eat from the garden. Trade at the post was good.

Sikwayi went to a pile of seasoned wood that he always kept beside the cabin.

"Today I shall start to make a chair," he said. "A fine chair like the one I saw in the white man's cabin the other day. Would you like such a chair, Mother?"

"That will be good," said Wur-teh. She looked at Sikwayi proudly. No other cabin in Taskigi had furniture to match hers.

Suddenly there was a cry in the forest near by. Sikwayi and Wur-teh looked up. An Indian came staggering into the clearing. Blood flowed from a wound in his head, and he looked ready to drop from weariness.

"Americans!" he gasped. "The Americans are coming! Fly to the hills!"

Wur-teh shrieked and ran for the cabin. For a moment Sikwayi stood frozen with astonishment and fear. Then he sprang forward to help the wounded man.

"What is it? What has happened?" Sikwayi cried. "Why are the Americans coming?"

He helped the wounded man to the cabin and gave him a drink of water.

For a moment or two the man sat gasping for breath. At last he said, "You know the Americans are fighting to drive the English out of America."

"Yes," Sikwayi said. "They sent a man here to ask us to help them."

"And we refused," the wounded man added. "The Americans are angry because we decided to help the English. They have sent an army over the mountains to punish us."

"But why shouldn't we help the English?" Sikwayi cried. "They do not take our lands away from us as the Americans do."

"True. But the Americans did not want us to help the English." The man struggled to his feet. "I must go. I must warn the others."

"Let me go!" cried Sikwayi eagerly.

"No. Go to the hills with your mother. Only the braves will stay." The man ran off, staggering with fatigue.

Sikwayi watched until the man was out of sight. Then, with a feeling of dread, he turned back to the cabin.

Wur-teh was flying about, trying to pack the things that would be needed in the mountains.

"We shall need food most," she said as she packed some dried venison, or deer meat, and some parched corn. She filled a deerskin bag with bear's grease.

"But the sheep and chickens and the cow!" Sikwayi said. "What about them?"

Wur-teh shook her head sadly. "We shall have to leave them. We can take nothing else."

Sikwayi stood for a moment in the doorway, looking around the cabin. All the trading goods, all the furs and skins, all the gains of all the years of work must be left behind. His heart was

44

heavy, and his eyes were dark with sorrow. A tear rolled down his cheek. He must leave his beloved apple trees behind!

Then he brightened. The Americans had no quarrel with his orchard. They could not carry the trees away with them. Surely they would leave the orchard alone.

"Come, my son," Wur-teh said gently. "We must hurry to the village."

With their belongings flung over their shoulders, Wur-teh and Sikwayi started for the village. From other cabins around the walls of Taskigi came frightened mothers with tiny children and babies on their backs. Old men and women came hobbling along with the sorrowful eyes of those who never expected to see their homes again. Several boys and girls of Sikwayi's age, who did not understand the danger, raced about laughing and yelling.

Sikwayi and Wur-teh walked along beside

Woodpecker, the chief of the village, and his grandson, Black Fox. They were silent, each one busy with his own thoughts.

At last Sikwayi broke the silence. "I wish we knew what the people of Towsee were doing," he said to Woodpecker.

Woodpecker's eyes grew sad.

"In times of trouble among our people it is every village for itself," he said. "The Cherokees are wise in many things, but not in that."

IN THE NAME OF KITUWAH

From the village Sikwayi and the others followed the path to a favorite hunting spot far up in the mountains. Sikwayi, Lone Bear, and Black Fox had gone there often.

"We know a cave," Sikwayi said to Woodpecker and Wur-teh. "It will be a fine place to hide from the Americans."

46

"That is good," Woodpecker said, pleased. He dropped back to tell some of the others who were coming behind.

By the time the villagers reached the cave, evening had come. The cave was warm and sheltered and large enough for all.

Lone Bear and his grandfather were already there. The people of Towsee had fled, too. Sikwayi was glad to know that Lone Bear was safe. Lone Bear was glad to see Sikwayi.

"Two hunters from our village saw the Americans coming," Lone Bear said. "They came back and told the braves of the village. The braves went out to fight the Americans. The old men and women and children made ready to come to the mountains." Lone Bear kicked a stone angrily. "I wanted to go with the braves. Instead, I had to come here and hide."

"Your time will come," his grandfather said. "You must wait and make ready."

"Wait! Wait!" cried Lone Bear. "I am tired of waiting. I want to fight!"

Sikwayi looked at his friend curiously. That was another way in which he, Sikwayi, was different from his friends. Perhaps it was because of his lame leg, but he wasn't waiting impatiently until he became a warrior.

"I hope our braves beat the Americans," Lone Bear went on. "I hope they drive the Americans back where they belong."

Sikwayi shook his head. "I do not think the braves will," he said. "There are too many Americans for small bands of Indians to beat. I think it would take all the Cherokees fighting together to stop them."

"But how can we get all the Cherokees to fight together?" demanded Lone Bear.

"I don't know," Sikwayi answered.

Sikwayi and Wur-teh and the others stayed in the cave for several days. Three sentinels or guards went out. One stayed hidden not far from Taskigi. Another stayed farther up the mountain. Still another camped on a rocky point near the cave.

Everyone waited for a signal from the lookout place. Such a signal would mean that it was safe to go home.

While they waited, Sikwayi, Lone Bear, Black Fox, and the other boys hunted. They brought back fresh meat to roast over a sheltered campfire. It was a welcome change from dried venison and parched corn.

In the shelter of the cave the villagers were warm and dry. It was spring, so no one suffered from the cold. But everyone wondered what was happening in the villages.

Early one morning the sentinel brought word that it was safe to go home. Everyone laughed and sang. Sikwayi made up a "Going-Back-Home" song and sang it loudly.

But along with the joy was fear.

"What shall we find when we return?" Woodpecker asked softly.

"Why, we'll find our homes, our gardens, and our cattle," some said.

Others were not so sure.

Woodpecker led his people down the mountainside. Parting at a fork in the trail, some went to Taskigi, some to Towsee.

"We will see each other soon," Sikwayi and Lone Bear promised each other.

Sikwayi, Wur-teh, Woodpecker, and the others neared Taskigi. Before they reached it, Woodpecker said, "I smell burning wood."

"I see smoke!" cried Sikwayi.

Sure enough, wisps of smoke were rising above the treetops. All the villagers ran toward the village. When they reached the clearing, they stopped short, horrified by what they saw.

The whole village, cabins, palisades, and coun-

cil house, lay in smoking ruins. The gardens were trampled down. The cattle, sheep, hogs, and chickens were gone.

Sikwayi's heart sank with fear. He turned and ran toward his mother's cabin. When he reached the clearing, he stopped and cried out in grief.

The cabin was burned to the ground. The garden was ruined. But worst of all, his beloved apple trees lay on the ground, chopped down by his own father's people.

In that moment Sikwayi's heart was filled with bitterness. "A Cherokee I will be to the end of my days!" he cried.

Some time later, all the villagers gathered before the ruins of the council house. Woodpecker began to speak.

"In the name of Kituwah, the Holy Place in the mountains from which all Cherokees came," he said solemnly, "we must build again."

Peace Town

THE LEADING town of the Cherokees was Chota. It, too, was on the Little Tennessee River, but it was several miles east of Taskigi. The Americans had not touched Chota because it was the Peace Town of the Cherokees, a kind of sacred or holy place to the whole nation.

Soon after Sikwayi and the others had returned to Taskigi, a message came from the principal chiefs of Chota.

"We will help the destroyed villages rebuild," the message said. "We will give all the seed we can spare so that our relatives and friends may replant their gardens. We will also give them all the cattle we can spare so that they can rebuild their herds."

Sikwayi and Black Fox went with Woodpecker and others to get the promised seeds and cattle.

Of all the things Sikwayi and Wur-teh had lost, Sikwayi missed his orchard most.

"I hope they will give us apple seeds," he said as he walked along beside Woodpecker.

"The people of Chota will give us apple seeds if they have them," Woodpecker answered.

Sikwayi's youthful face looked thoughtful. "You know, Woodpecker," he said seriously, "this sharing shows that the Cherokees *can* work together when they wish."

Woodpecker nodded. "That is true. It is sad that we do not want to work together more often. After all, a trouble shared is a trouble cut in half."

Sikwayi wished that all Cherokees were as wise as Woodpecker.

Sikwayi was almost happy as he walked with

Woodpecker that morning. He loved the piney smell of the woods and the shadowy paths. He enjoyed watching the squirrels dart across the path ahead of him and run up trees, flicking their long tails. He enjoyed the busy chipmunks and the sweet songs of birds.

"How I love our mountains!" he said. "I know there is no better place to live."

"It has been our home for a long, long time," Woodpecker replied.

"And now the Americans would take it away from us!" cried Black Fox angrily.

"Yes, the Americans want land," Woodpecker agreed. "They cannot get enough land. And they want to *own* it. They want to say, 'This land is ours. Keep off!'"

Sikwayi was puzzled. "But how can they do that? The forests and mountains and streams belong to the Great Spirit."

"Of course," Woodpecker said. "The Great

Spirit loaned them to us to use as long as there are Cherokees alive. But the Americans do not believe that. They will not live with the land as we do, by hunting and fishing as well as farming. They would cut down the forests to make fields and drive all the game away. That is why we must drive them out of our lands. They will not let us live as we wish to live."

"How I wish I were old enough to be a warrior!" Black Fox cried. "I would drive the Americans out if I had to do it alone!"

Sikwayi was silent as he limped along beside his friends. He felt as much a Cherokee as Black Fox. But he would never be a warrior and he knew it. He would have to think of some other way to help his mother's people.

At last Woodpecker and his group reached the palisaded town of Chota. It was larger than Taskigi. There were many log cabins and a big council house in the center of the village. As the travelers entered the town, dogs ran toward them, barking. Then, wagging their tails, the dogs followed the travelers to the council house.

The council house was a big dome-shaped building covered with earth. Inside, a fire burned at all times. The smoke escaped through a hole in the center of the roof. The light was dim. Sikwayi blinked a few times before he could see the inside of the building clearly.

One of the chiefs came forward. Sikwayi greeted him happily. His name was Old Turkey, and he was Sikwayi's uncle. He had married into the Ani'tsis'kwa or Bird clan, one of the seven Cherokee clans.

Old Turkey asked Woodpecker why he and the others had come.

"You offered to give us seeds," Woodpecker said. "We have come for them. Our homes are gone. Our corn was ruined. All our cows, pigs, sheep, and chickens were run off or killed."

"And my apple orchard was cut down," Si-kwayi added indignantly.

Old Turkey shook his head sadly. "What a waste," he said.

He led them to a smaller building near by. Inside Sikwayi saw rows of baskets, each basket full of corn, bean, squash, or pumpkin seeds.

"These will help you replant your gardens," Old Turkey said. He handed Sikwayi a small leather pouch.

"In this pouch are apple seeds," he added, smiling. "I am happy to give them to one who I know will treat them with care."

Sikwayi's eyes shone with joy. He could plant an apple orchard again. He reached for the little pouch and tucked it carefully inside his cotton shirt.

"I shall plant these seeds as soon as I get home," he said. He patted the pouch lovingly. "I shall water and tend them carefully. When they grow to seedlings I shall give some of them to others who want them."

"That will be to every family in the village," Woodpecker said with a twinkle in his eyes.

Next Old Turkey gave Woodpecker and his fellow villagers a cow, several sheep, some pigs, and a number of chickens.

"We will be busy driving these animals back home!" Sikwayi cried in delight.

"It will be worth it," grinned Black Fox.

As they were getting ready to leave, Old Turkey said, "The principal chiefs are meeting this afternoon in the council house. They are going to talk of ways to keep the Americans from getting more Cherokee land. Would you care to stay and listen?"

Sikwayi could have whooped for joy. Would he like to stay? Did a bear like honey? He looked anxiously at Woodpecker.

"We shall be happy to come to the meeting in the council house," the old man said. "I would like to hear what the chiefs have to say."

THE LOST CHEROKEES

The principal chiefs sat in a circle around the fire in the center of the council house. Sikwayi and the other onlookers sat on seats farther back, around the wall.

When everyone was seated, Old Turkey rose.

"We will now have the reading of the wampum," he said solemnly.

Another old chief came forward. He carried a length of wampum. Sikwayi leaned forward to hear better.

Wampum was made of beads and string. It was used as money. It was used in the making of treaties. It was also used to record important things that had happened in the past.

Only learned men could read the messages recorded in wampum. The colors of the beads had certain meanings. The shapes of the beads and the way the beads were arranged had other meanings. Readers of the wampum kept the secrets of their trade to themselves, just as the medicine men did.

The old man began to read or recite. He knew the story told by the wampum by heart. It was the story of the Cherokees, who called themselves the Real People.

The wampum told how powerful the Cherokees had been in the old days. It sang of the glory of their ancient home in Kituwah, high in the Smoky Mountains. It told of the wanderings of the people and of the brave deeds of their warriors. It praised the wisdom and courage of their great chiefs.

Sikwayi grew warm with pride as he listened. It was good to be a Cherokee.

The wampum told next of the coming of the first white men. They had been looking for silver and gold. The Cherokees could not understand why the white men valued these things so highly. Silver and gold were good only to make ornaments for the fingers and ears.

The white men were angry when they found so little of the metals. They marched off, threatening to return and destroy the Cherokees. Many years later they did return. Then the troubles of the Cherokees began.

The wampum ended with the story of the Lost Cherokees. Many years ago, it was said, some of the Cherokees had become angry because the white men kept taking their land. They had moved to some unknown part of the West, beyond the Mississippi River. They had never been heard from since.

The reading ended. The old chief rolled the wampum and sat down. The principal chiefs and the visitors looked sad. Some of the older ones had had relatives and friends among the Lost Cherokees. What had become of them?

Sikwayi felt especially sad. His father's people had made these kinsmen leave.

Old Turkey rose.

"Now, my brothers," he said solemnly, "we come to the important part of our meeting." His dark eyes swept searchingly over the principal chiefs. "Are we going to try to stop the white men? Or shall we let them take our lands?"

"Stop them! Stop them!" came the reply from many throats.

Again Old Turkey looked at the chiefs.

"Then first we must stop our own chiefs from giving away their villages for worthless trinkets!" he roared. "You know as well as I do that many are doing this."

An angry murmur went through the council house. How well the Cherokees knew this!

Another chief arose.

"Old Turkey is right," he said. "Some of our chiefs are selling land that does not belong to them. They sign treaties with the white men that affect us all. But they do not tell us about these treaties until it is too late."

"Treaties mean nothing to the white man," another said. "He signs them one day and breaks them the next."

"That is true. But some of our chiefs still fall for the white man's flattery," Old Turkey said. "The white man knows that by dealing with one chief at a time he will get our land."

"We must stop it!" someone cried.

"How?" Old Turkey wanted to know. "Sometimes weeks go by before we know that a chief has sold another village. Then it is too late to do anything about it."

Old Turkey was right, and all his listeners knew it. This had been going on for some time. And the principal chiefs were helpless to stop it.

"If all the Cherokees would band together, we could refuse to sell any land to the white man," Old Turkey said.

"How can we band together?" asked the others. "We do not have the magic of the white man's talking leaves."

Sikwayi lifted his head in surprise. Talking leaves? What did the man mean?

"Perhaps all of us should have gone west with our kinsmen, the Lost Cherokees," Old Turkey said sadly.

"No! No! We will stay!" cried the others.

Sikwayi was silent. He had not heard Old Turkey's last remark. He was wondering what talking leaves could possibly be.

Powerful Magic

THE drumming started softly.

Sikwayi's heart began to pound. Would he make a mistake before all the people of Taskigi? He smoothed down the feathers of his eagle costume and waited. His fear went away. He was a good dancer, even though he was lame, and he knew it. He had practiced hard. He knew every step of his part in the Pigeon Dance.

From each side of the Council Rock came four dancers. Going in opposite directions, they started dancing in a circle around the bright fire. They went with a flat-footed trot, gently, timidly, like the pigeons they were supposed to be. The arms of each dancer were raised in the air like wings.

All the dancers bent forward a little. Their heads were turned toward the sky. Fear was on their faces. A quarter way around the circle they stopped. They searched the sky as their hands fluttered like wings.

The drums grew louder. Up and down the dancers went, bending at the knees eight times. On they went, timidly, fearfully.

The eagle? Where was the eagle?

When the two lines of dancers met, the dancers stopped again and looked upward. Up and down they went again, eight times.

Then the lines separated and went on around the fire. In and out they went, stopping to study the sky. The drumming swelled. The pigeons formed a half circle around the fire, opposite the Council Rock.

Sikwayi watched and waited. As the pigeons

stopped, he raised his arms with their feathered sleeves. He swooped into the ring.

"The eagle!" the watchers murmured. "What a fine eagle the son of Wur-teh makes."

Swiftly Sikwayi made a figure eight about the fire. He trotted lightly, hardly touching his toes to the ground. This way and that he swayed. First one arm slanted upward and then the other.

The murmuring went on. This was the finest eagle that had ever danced the Pigeon Dance! Sikwayi heard what the people were saying and danced better than ever.

It was Corn Festival time. The village of Taskigi was celebrating. Its people had much to be happy about. The corn crop was good, with plenty laid away for the winter. The war between the English and the Americans was over. The Cherokees had been beaten along with the English. That did not mean much. All the Cherokees wanted was for the Americans to leave them alone. They wanted to live in peace in their villages, hunting and tending their fields.

Sikwayi was a young man now. It was a happy time for him, too.

Twice Taskigi had been destroyed by the Americans. Twice he and Wur-teh had rebuilt their cabin. Twice he had replanted his orchard and watched it grow.

The last time had been the hardest. For that time Chota had been destroyed as well. Sikwayi and Wur-teh had had a hard time finding seeds with which to replant the garden and orchard.

Thompson, the friendly white settler, had felt bad about the destruction of Taskigi. He had given Sikwayi apple and peach seeds as well as seeds for the garden. He had given seeds to others in the village, too. He had helped the villagers as much as he could.

Now some fine young trees were growing in the orchard. The Cherokees' troubles were over.

Sikwayi and Wur-teh and the people of Taskigi need never be afraid again.

Up and down before the trembling pigeons Sikwayi swooped triumphantly. Back and forth before each one he trotted, as he had seen the white settler's wesa play with a field mouse before devouring it. The pigeons crouched down. They fluttered their hands and rolled their eyes as if in fear.

Sikwayi stopped before one pigeon. The pigeon grinned faintly at him, trying not to let the grin show. It was Sikwayi's friend, Black Fox.

The eagle winked at the pigeon. It danced excitedly back and forth before the chosen victim. Then a wing of the eagle darted out and seized the pigeon. Firmly the trembling pigeon was drawn out into the center of the ring. It was helpless in the eagle's strong grip.

The other pigeons fluttered around Black Fox. They tried to protect him. But they could not win a fight with an eagle. They fell back and left the pigeon to its fate.

The eagle swayed and swooped around the frightened pigeon. Never had there been such a frightened pigeon before. The eagle threatened. The pigeon crouched down in fear. Then, with a flourish of its wings, the eagle grabbed the pigeon and dragged it out of the ring.

The pigeons hung their heads in shame. What cowards they were! They had not helped one of their kind when he was in trouble. They tiptoed out of the ring.

Behind the Council Rock Sikwayi and Black Fox hugged each other. They laughed with joy.

"What an eagle you make!" cried Black Fox.

"What an actor and dancer you are, Black Fox!" Sikwayi replied. "No pigeon was ever so frightened before."

Suddenly the two boys heard a loud pounding outside the palisade. They straightened up. Out-

side the closed gate a voice roared in English,
"Open up! Fast!"

TALKING LEAVES

The gate of Taskigi swung open. Outside the
wall were four white men, mounted on horses.

"We want to talk to the chief of the village,"
said one of the men.

Slowly, and with great dignity, Woodpecker
came forward.

"I am chief of Taskigi," he said.

The white man who had spoken looked down
at the chief. From his pocket he took something
white. His face was grim.

A crowd was gathering just inside the gate.
Sikwayi edged forward. He was careful not to
tear his eagle costume. Wur-teh had spent many
days sewing the feathers on it. It must last for
many Pigeon Dances.

Sikwayi was very close to Woodpecker and the white men now. He listened closely. What did the white men want? The Cherokees had done nothing wrong. What *could* the Americans want?

Fear stole over Sikwayi. It must be land! The Americans were here to drive the people of Taskigi out of their homes. But surely the Americans could not do that. The Cherokees were not at war with them now.

The American held out the white thing he had taken from the pocket of his deerskin shirt. He shook it before Woodpecker's face. It looked like a piece of birchbark. On it were some strange-looking black marks.

Sikwayi was puzzled. The marks looked like chicken tracks. He had never seen anything like them before. What could they be?

Again the American waved the white thing in front of Woodpecker's face. It rattled like birchbark, too.

"This is an order from our government," he said. "It tells the people of Taskigi that they must move away."

A look of astonishment crossed Woodpecker's face. "Move!" he cried. "Why must we move? This has always been our home."

The American frowned. "The land does not belong to you," he growled.

Woodpecker smiled. "I know that," he said. "The land belongs to the Great Spirit. But he has said that we could use it."

The American listened impatiently. Then he shrugged his shoulders.

"This land belongs to us," he said. He waved his hand at the three men with him. "Our government says so. It says so right here."

He pointed a bony finger at the marks on the white thing in his hand. Sikwayi's eyebrows went up in surprise. The white man was saying that the thing in his hand could talk!

"You and your people had better get ready to leave," the American went on. "Right away."

Despair and helplessness clouded Woodpecker's face. He stood for a moment, unable to speak. Then he drew himself up proudly.

"This is our home," he said quietly. "The Great Spirit has let us live here for many years. We will not go. Close the gate."

Sikwayi and several other young men jumped to do Woodpecker's bidding. They closed the gate of the palisade in the faces of the white men. The white men yelled in anger.

"It won't do you any good to close the gate! You'll have to leave anyway!"

Woodpecker turned to face his people.

"Everyone must stay inside the village walls until the white men leave," he said.

Cold fear crept up Sikwayi's spine. The white men were angry. When angry, they would destroy. He looked at Woodpecker questioningly.

"Will they burn down our cabin again?" he asked. "Will they chop down my apple trees?"

Woodpecker's eyes were filled with pain. "I do not think so," he replied. "I think this time the white men want those things for themselves."

Sikwayi felt better. The white men would never get his home or eat his apples. He and Wur-teh would not move.

"What is the white thing the American carried?" he asked curiously. "The thing which he said could talk?"

"It is one of the white men's talking leaves," Woodpecker said sadly. "With them the Americans have forced the people of several of our villages to move. Then they took over the land and cabins and crops without even paying our people for them."

Sikwayi was astonished. "The white man's talking leaves must truly be magic," he said.

"Powerful magic," Woodpecker replied.

"The magic of the talking leaves must be a gift of the white man's God," the people of Taskigi said to one another. "We have no magic as powerful as that."

All night the villagers stayed inside the palisade, wondering what would happen to them.

Sikwayi lay awake and wondered. "Are the talking leaves really magic?" he asked himself. "Are they a gift from the white man's God? Could they drive our people away from home?"

Then he thought, "But that cannot be true! I was close to the white men and saw the strange marks on the leaves."

Perhaps the marks were pictures like the ones he and Mr. Thompson had drawn in the dirt. Or perhaps they were meaningful signs or symbols like those on a band of wampum.

Suddenly Sikwayi sat up. Excitement flashed through him. That was it! The talking leaves

79

were only a clever way the white men had of telling one another things!

He sank back on his bed, relieved. If that were so, then the talking leaves were no more magic than the wesa had been.

Carefully he smoothed down the feathers of his eagle costume. It was all he had to wear until the white men left. His other clothes were at the trading post. Soon he was sound asleep.

The next day the white men returned. They pounded on the gate. "We want to talk to your chief again!" the leader shouted.

The gate opened. Woodpecker went forward to talk to the Americans. The leader of the Americans again waved the talking leaves in the old chief's face.

"Our government says this land is ours," the man said. "You and your people must go!"

"We will not," Woodpecker answered firmly.

"Then we will burn down your town!"

"You will burn us with it," Woodpecker replied. Once more he ordered his people to close the gate and keep the white men out.

All that day and night the people stayed inside the walls of the village. They were worried and frightened.

"Would the white men burn the village while we are in it?" they wondered.

"I think not," Woodpecker said.

Next morning the white men came to the gate again. They were angrier than ever now. With them were other white men and their families.

"Move now and don't cause us any trouble," the leader ordered. "If you do you'll never be bothered again."

Woodpecker looked at him with scorn. "A white man's promise is as lasting as a ripple in a brook," he said.

The white man's face turned red.

"We've been patient enough with you Indians!" he yelled. "We have soldiers coming. If you don't move willingly, our soldiers will drive you off this land."

Woodpecker was silent. He stared straight ahead for a moment. Then he bowed his head.

"We will move," he said sadly. "If your soldiers are coming we have no choice."

Turning to his people, he told them to get ready to move. They all went sadly to their cabins, Wur-teh and Sikwayi among them. A lump was in Sikwayi's throat as he looked for the last time at the cabin and the garden and orchard behind the cabin. This was the only home he had ever known.

A wagon stopped in front of the cabin. A white man and his wife and four children climbed down from it.

"This is a mighty nice place," the man said, grinning with pleasure. "We'll take this one."

He went to the door of the cabin.

"Just take your clothes and get out," he told Sikwayi and Wur-teh. "My family is moving in."

Fury rose in Sikwayi. He must obey the settler's order. But the thought of the white man's unfairness almost choked him.

"I'm glad *I'm* Cherokee!" he muttered. He and Wur-teh gathered up some clothes and food.

Suddenly he remembered the silver coins. He could take that much with him. The white man would never know.

He made sure no one was looking. Then he took the pouch of coins from behind a pile of furs in a corner of the cabin. There must have been fifty coins in the pouch. He tucked the pouch inside his shirt.

He and Wur-teh started out. They did not know where to go. Along the way they met others who did not know where to go either.

Sikwayi's heart was heavy. "We Cherokees are like the pigeons," he thought. "The Americans are like the eagle. It is easy for a strong eagle to frighten and conquer the pigeons."

Young
Craftsman

WITH A pair of tongs Sikwayi held the silver
coin over the flame of a small forge. He turned
it over and around. He waited until the head
of the English king began to soften and run. He
laid the coin quickly on a tiny anvil. With a
hammer he began to flatten it.

Tap, tap, tap. As he tapped, he sang softly.

> "Here I sit in my store all day,
> And heat the silver
> And melt it
> And hammer and shape it
> Into pretty things for my people."

The door of the cabin opened, and a neighbor, Flying Leaf, came in. He carried a big chunk of beeswax. Traders liked beeswax, for they could sell it to candlemakers for a good price.

Flying Leaf coughed softly, but Sikwayi did not look up. Flying Leaf looked at Wur-teh, who smiled. They both knew that Sikwayi had not seen or heard Flying Leaf enter the cabin. They knew that he was lost in his world of Making-Things. He often was, these days.

Flying Leaf traded his beeswax for an ax. Then he went to the corner where Sikwayi was working. He looked over Sikwayi's shoulder.

Sikwayi went on hammering and singing. He pounded the silver until it was the thickness he wanted. Then he began to shape it into a buckle. From time to time he held it over the fire again to heat and soften it.

Nodding in approval, Flying Leaf glanced around the trading post. He saw a number of things that Sikwayi had made. There were bracelets and buttons, buckles and earrings. The Cherokees liked Sikwayi's things and often traded their furs and beeswax for them.

Three years had passed since Sikwayi and Wur-teh had left Taskigi. They were now living in Etowah, a Valley Town not far from Tellico. The Valley Towns were farther south and west than Taskigi.

Sikwayi and his mother were happy in Etowah. Many of their old neighbors lived close by.

Sikwayi had built a nice log cabin with a puncheon or split log floor. Over the creek beside the cabin he had built another springhouse. He had also made a churn and a milk skimmer for his mother. He had seen these things in the homes of white settlers.

"He looks like an Indian," Woodpecker told Wur-teh once. "He feels he is an Indian. But he thinks like a white man. He dreams and works like a white man."

No one would have dared tell Sikwayi that. To himself he was all Cherokee. But while his mother's people were calm and slow to show emotion, Sikwayi was never still. His feelings spilled over often.

The apple trees in his new orchard were four feet high now. In a cleared patch behind the cabin grew a fine garden. It was bound by a snake-fence to keep out the cow and sheep and pigs. Around the cabin grew morning-glories and sunflowers.

In one corner of the cabin stood a spinning wheel. Soon Wur-teh would have a loom. Then she could weave warm cloth from the wool of their own sheep.

Sikwayi's people respected him for his many skills as a craftsman. At the same time, however, they thought him a little queer.

Flying Leaf turned and quietly left the trading post. Wur-teh went back to her churning.

Sikwayi lifted the buckle and smiled with satisfaction. It wasn't so handsome a buckle as his friend and teacher, Tsun-ga'ni, could make. But with the help of Excels-All-Others, Sikwayi's work was improving.

He would keep on working and trying to do better. Some day, he promised himself, he would be the best of all Cherokee silversmiths!

GIVE IN OR FIGHT?

A few days later Sikwayi strode down the trail toward the cabin of Excels-All-Others. He would sit beside the master silversmith and watch him work. He could learn much that way.

In Sikwayi's pocket was the buckle he had finished. After Flying Leaf had left, Sikwayi had picked up his engraving tool. With it he had worked a design around the edge of the buckle.

He had spent days planning the design. He

had used an oak leaf and an acorn, repeating them again and again. Before putting the design on the buckle, he had drawn it many times in the dirt with a stick. When it looked just right, he had stored it away in his mind.

When he had finished engraving the buckle, he had polished it. He had rubbed it with wood ashes and a piece of soft buckskin until it shone.

Excels-All-Others held the buckle in his hand and studied it. He turned it round and round. Then a pleased smile crossed his face.

"You have done well, Sikwayi," he said.

Sikwayi beamed with pleasure. "But I still have much to learn," he said. He sat down beside the workbench. His sharp eyes missed nothing as Excels-All-Others went back to work on a silver snuffbox.

"A white man in Tellico asked me to make this for him," Excels-All-Others said. He picked up his engraving tool and leaned over, his face close to the box.

Sikwayi admired the design the old man was working on. Around the edge of the snuffbox was a feathery border. In the center was a butterfly with outstretched wings. How light and delicate, but sure, the lines were!

"Some day I shall do as well," Sikwayi thought.

Near by were several knives, forks, and spoons. They too were made of silver and had beautiful designs on the handles. Excels-All-Others made and sold many of them, chiefly to white people.

Suddenly, as Sikwayi was admiring the engraving, a friend of the silversmith burst into the cabin. Fear and anger were on his face.

"They have done it again!" he cried.

Excels-All-Others turned. "Who have done what?" he asked quietly.

"The Americans have burned three more villages!" The newcomer dropped down on a stool. It was really a section of log turned on end. Excels-All-Others did not have chairs in his cabin as Sikwayi and Wur-teh did.

Sikwayi's heart missed a beat. His father's people were up to their old tricks again. What would they do next?

"Why should they do that?" Sikwayi asked. "We are at peace with them."

The man leaned forward. His red cotton shirt glowed in a shaft of sunlight coming through the window.

"We are at peace with them for the time be-

ing," the man said. "But the Chicamaugas refuse to make peace."

Dismay crossed the faces of Sikwayi and
Excels-All-Others. They would not be surprised
by anything the Chicamaugas did.

The Chicamaugas were a group of Cherokees
who had refused to make peace with the Americans. They had refused to sign the white man's
treaty. They had moved beyond Lookout Mountain and settled in their own towns along Chica-
mauga Creek. They hated the white men bitterly
and fought them whenever they could.

"The Chicamaugas burned a white village a
few days ago," the man went on. "The white men
burned ours in revenge."

"But we are not Chicamaugas!" cried Sikwayi.
"We have given the Americans all they asked for.
We try to live in peace with them. Why do they
burn our villages?"

"To the white man an Indian is an Indian,"

Excels-All-Others said quietly. "It matters not to which tribe he belongs."

Shame swept through Sikwayi. More than ever he wished that no white man's blood flowed through his veins. He picked up his buckle and rose to his feet.

"You are leaving so soon?" Excels-All-Others asked in surprise.

"I must be alone with my thoughts," Sikwayi answered. He went out the door and walked slowly toward home.

What were the Cherokees to do? They had tried everything in their effort to get along with the white man. Was it better to give in or to fight? The Indians seemed to lose, no matter what they did.

Sikwayi wanted to do something to prove his loyalty to his mother's people. But what could he do? What could any man do alone, without the help of all Cherokees?

Some days later Sikwayi was seated at his workbench. He was engraving a sunflower design on the handle of a silver spoon. Although it was a white man's flower, Sikwayi liked the sunflower. He liked its shape and its color.

Sikwayi was so busy that he did not hear anyone enter the cabin. But he did hear the familiar voice when it said, over his shoulder, "Soup should taste much better when eaten from such a beautiful spoon."

He turned to see Woodpecker standing behind him. Woodpecker was older and more wrinkled now. But he was as dear a friend as ever. So was Black Fox, who stood beside him.

"It is for Wur-teh," Sikwayi said, holding the spoon up. "She wished for one."

"And that was all she had to do to get her son to make one," Woodpecker said with a smile.

The old man took the spoon and looked it over.

It was small and gracefully shaped and perfectly balanced. It was work to be proud of.

"It is a fine spoon," he said, and laid it down. From the look on the old man's face Sikwayi could tell that something was bothering him.

"What is wrong?" Sikwayi asked anxiously.

Woodpecker shook his head. "It is the white men again," he said, his voice quivering. "They came with their talking leaves to Crow Town. They forced Black Crow and his people to leave. Then they moved in."

Sikwayi gasped. A look of pain filled his eyes.

"But the people of Crow Town moved from another village just a year ago!" he cried. "The white men told them then that they would never be bothered again."

Woodpecker nodded. "Just as we were promised when we left Taskigi," he said sadly.

Sikwayi whirled to face his old friend. "Do you mean they might make us move again?" he

demanded. "They might make us leave our new home in Etowah?"

Woodpecker sighed. "They might," he said. "Their talking leaves are powerful magic."

After trading a muskrat pelt for salt, Woodpecker and Black Fox left. Sikwayi watched the proud old chief go down the path. It would kill him to have to move his people again!

Sikwayi did not wish to move again either. He loved Etowah.

"What is wrong with the white men?" he wondered. "Is there no honor among them? They make promises one day and break them the next day."

He looked at his workbench. Then he looked at his small forge, at the goatskin bellows, at his hammers and tongs. A feeling of anger rose in him. His people needed help. And here he was wasting his time making trinkets of silver!

Without a backward glance, he walked out of the cabin. He headed for the deep forest beyond his garden. Finally he sat down on a fallen log beside a creek. The forest was quiet and shadowy. Now and then a bird sang or a squirrel chattered somewhere in a tree. The leaves sighed as a wind passed overhead. But Sikwayi heard and saw nothing, though his eyes and ears were open. He was deep in thought.

"How can I help my people?" he wondered. "Should I join the Chicamaugas? But there are not enough Cherokees to hold back the endless stream of white men who want our lands.

"What makes the white men so strong? Is it their talking leaves? Perhaps if the Cherokees had talking leaves they could work together. If they worked together, they might force the white men to be more fair."

At this point an idea came to him. He jumped up from the log. With a pointed stick he made scratches in the dirt. They looked like the ones he had seen on the talking leaves. But what did they mean?

He drew a picture of a deer running, using straight lines. To an Indian the picture would mean running deer. Were the scratches on the talking leaves picture writing?

He shook his head. The white man's talking leaves did more than that. They really talked.

The white man put words down on them just as he would say the words.

Sikwayi sank back on the log. Cherokee words could never be put down with marks or lines. They were made up of pieces of words and many words put together. Besides, different Cherokee tribes spoke a little differently.

Sikwayi sighed and dropped his stick. A squirrel chattered again overhead and he laughed grimly. It would be as easy to put down the chattering of a squirrel as the talk of a Cherokee!

The Accident

IT WAS late fall of the same year. The mountainsides were bright with autumn leaves.

Sikwayi stood for a moment in the doorway of his cabin in Etowah. The smell of woodsmoke was in the air. Behind him a warm fire crackled and snapped in the fireplace.

A dreamy smile crossed his face. "This is the best time of the year," he said.

Wur-teh laughed. "Might one reason be that the hunting season is here?" she asked softly.

"That's partly right," Sikwayi agreed. "I like to hunt. I like to live in the open and sleep by a campfire under the trees. When I'm out in the forest alone, hunting, I have plenty of time to think about things."

He smiled again. "I am not a bad hunter, you know," he added.

"You are a good hunter," Wur-teh replied. "You belong to the Red Paint clan, and the men of our clan have always been good hunters."

She turned and began to stir the contents of an iron pot hanging over the fire. As he watched her, a look of worry crossed Sikwayi's face. For some time now his mother had not seemed herself. The glow was gone from her cheeks and the brightness from her eyes. She had said nothing, but Sikwayi knew that she was not well.

"Isn't it time for you and your friends to go hunting?" Wur-teh asked presently.

For a few moments Sikwayi made no answer. Then in a strange voice he said, "I may not go."

"Not go! Why not? How will you get the hunters' best furs if you are not there to trade?

You *must* go, my son. We need the furs you will bring home."

Sikwayi still hesitated.

"Don't worry about me," she went on. "I will be all right. Look." She pointed to dried rings of pumpkins and squash hanging from the rafters above the fireplace. "I have plenty of food from the garden. There is plenty of firewood beside the cabin. Our friends and neighbors will stop in from time to time to trade."

"But—but what if the white men come? What would you do?"

"White men!" Wur-teh laughed. "I am not afraid of the white men. They will not want this little bit of ground we use."

"Well—I have made a new bow and some new arrows. And my friends are leaving today."

"Good! Pack the things you will need and go. I have made you a new woolen jacket and some new buckskin trousers and moccasins. Pack them all on the horse you bought the other day and go with your friends."

Sikwayi looked around the cabin. In a far corner stood his workbench, with his silversmithing tools neatly arranged on it. He had not used it much lately. Next to the bench, along the wall, were shelves on which the trading goods were kept. They were almost bare now, because most of the goods had been sold.

Sikwayi straightened his shoulders. His mother was right. He *must* go hunting. He must get more furs in order to get more trading goods for the post. His people needed the trading post.

With a cheerful smile, he ate his morning meal. He packed the things he would need and fastened the packs on the back of his horse. Then he mounted and rode off to join his friends.

Wur-teh stood in the doorway of the cabin, watching him. When he looked back, she waved.

"Have a good hunt, my son," she called.

"Instantly the Red Reed strikes you, in the very center of your soul! Instantly! *Yu!*" cried Sikwayi eagerly.

As he uttered the word *yu* he let the arrow go. It was important that he do that. If he did not, the arrow would not find its mark.

It was an old hunting prayer that he uttered, a prayer that had been handed down in his clan from the days when the Cherokees made their arrows from reeds. It was a powerful prayer. It had brought him many fine deer in the past.

Today he had parted from the other hunters. They had gone to trap some beavers at a beaver colony they had found. He had headed for this spot by a stream, where he had seen deer come to drink.

For a long while he had waited and watched, as silent as the tree behind which he stood. Finally a deer came, picking its way down the narrow trail. Sikwayi could tell by its antlers that it was a big buck. It was cautious and careful. It stopped several times, looking for danger. Its ears and the tip of its nose twitched.

Sikwayi was glad the wind was blowing from the deer toward him, and not the other way round. If the deer had scented him, it would have been off with twice the speed of his arrow.

It was a cold, windy day. A wet snow was falling and lay in patches on the fallen leaves.

The arrow sped on the word *yu*. The buck went down. The arrow had killed it instantly.

Sikwayi ran to the fallen deer. He knelt beside it with drawn knife.

"I am sorry to hurt you, my brother," he said softly. "Do not grieve. Little Deer will come soon to get you."

Little Deer was chief of all the deer in the forest, the Cherokees believed. When a hunter killed a deer and took the meat and skin, Little

Deer would come to the spot where his comrade had fallen. He would find a drop of its blood. From this drop he would cause another deer to spring.

The Cherokee hunter did not believe he had really killed the deer. But he knew the arrow had hurt it, so he always said he was sorry.

Swiftly Sikwayi skinned the deer. He cut up the meat. Then, staggering under his load, he started back to camp.

It was snowing harder now. He had trouble keeping the trail in sight. But he went on, head down, into the driving snow. He could not see three feet ahead of him.

Finally he drew near the camp. He could not see it. He could not even see the trail ahead of him. But he knew that in a few minutes he would be in camp and could warm himself before the fire. He was so tired by now that he was beginning to limp badly.

Suddenly the snow-covered ground gave way beneath him and he plunged downward. There was a sharp, burning pain in one leg, close to the knee. For an agonizing moment he hung motionless in air. Then, as the pain grew sharper, he turned and fell downward again.

When he came to, he found himself lying at the bottom of a deep pit. Close to the top above him, stakes had been driven into the sides of the pit. He had blundered off the trail and fallen into a bear trap that he and his friends had made the other day!

He tried to sit up but fell back with a cry of pain. Blood was pouring from a deep cut in his leg. In falling, he had been caught for a moment on one of the sharpened stakes.

He lay still for a moment. Then, in spite of the pain, he started to climb out. He must get back to camp before he bled too much.

It took him a long time to pull himself out of

the pit, but he did it somehow. Then he dragged himself slowly over the snow-covered ground. Twice his mind went blank. When his senses returned, he crawled on.

At last he saw the dim light of the campfire through the falling snow. He let out a yell.

Black Fox and Little Beaver came running. Soon they were bending over him, stemming the flow of blood. The stake had driven deep into the flesh behind his knee. The wound was bad, and Black Fox and Little Beaver knew it.

Sikwayi lay awake that night. His leg throbbed with pain. Something had told him not to come on this hunting trip. Should he have listened and stayed home?

HOMECOMING

"We must take you home," Black Fox said anxiously the next morning. "Wur-teh will know what to do for your leg. She can take care of you better than we can."

"She will know which herbs make the best healing potions," said Flying Leaf.

"She could have the shaman come," Little Beaver added. "He would sing and pray and make your leg well."

The shaman was the medicine man.

Sikwayi lay on a bearskin inside the bark hunting hut. His eyes were bright with fever, and his skin was hot to the touch. But he knew what he was doing.

"I will stay with you, my brothers," he said firmly. "I will not go home until the hunt is over. Don't worry about me. Just be thankful, as I am, that I injured my bad leg." He laughed painfully. "It was not a good leg anyway."

The others shook their heads.

"We could talk until the moon changes, but we will never change his mind," said Black Fox.

"He came to get furs and he will not leave until he has them."

Black Fox and Flying Leaf tried to make Sikwayi as comfortable as they could. Black Fox made broth from the deer meat. He stripped bark from a sweet-gum tree and boiled it. Then he poured the hot liquid over Sikwayi's wound.

Black Fox and Flying Leaf both nursed Sikwayi. They sang all the "Songs-to-Heal-By" that they knew. They sang each song four times to make sure that their singing would help.

Sikwayi was feverish for several days. His leg was bent under him in pain. Then the fever went away. But the pain in his leg did not.

As soon as he could, Sikwayi tried to sit up. When no one was looking, he tried to get to his feet. The moment his foot touched the ground, white-hot pain raced up his leg and he fell back on the bearskin.

Later he made a kind of crutch from the

branch of a hickory tree and taught himself to use it. Before long he was hobbling about on what he called his three legs.

The wound in his leg seemed to heal, but the flesh around it remained red and angry. But Sikwayi would not give up. With the help of his crutch he went hunting. He tended the traps he had made and set in the woods and along a stream. He bargained with his friends for furs.

Sikwayi could walk when the time came to return home. But his leg was stiff and his limp was worse than ever. He did not tell the others how much it hurt to walk, but they knew. They carried some of his furs. For long distances they made him ride.

Sikwayi was happy in spite of his leg. He had done what he had set out to do, and now he was going home. He could already see the happy look on Wur-teh's face when she saw the fine furs that he had collected.

When they reached the village, Sikwayi's friends packed most of his furs on the horse. The rest he would have to carry. But he did not have far to go, so he did not mind.

Bidding his friends good-by, Sikwayi limped off toward his cabin. When he came within sight of it, his heart skipped a beat. There was no smoke coming from the chimney, and the place looked empty.

"Mother!" he called. "Oh, Mother!"

There was no answer. Sikwayi quickened his steps. Then he saw Woodpecker waiting in the doorway. The old man's face was sad.

"What is it?" Sikwayi cried anxiously. "Where is my mother?"

Woodpecker put one hand on Sikwayi's shoulder. "Your mother has gone to the land of our ancestors," he said softly. "She died while you and your friends were away."

Sikwayi turned and sank down on the step.

114

For a long time he sat there on the doorstep, alone with his grief.

"My mother is gone," he thought. "What is there to live for now?"

Then he seemed to hear his mother's voice, saying what she had said so often before. "The Cherokees need your help. Help them in every way you can, my son."

Sikwayi rose and went into the cabin. He looked around. At least the white men had not come. He still had his home. He started a fire in the fireplace and unpacked his furs.

There was much work to be done.

New Ideas

ONE DAY as Sikwayi was passing the blacksmith shop in Tellico, he heard the smith hammering on the anvil. He stopped to watch.

The smith's name was Jenkins. As Sikwayi watched, Jenkins heated a horseshoe in the flames of the forge. He hammered the shoe on his anvil and nailed it on the hoof of a horse.

The horse belonged to a friend of Sikwayi named Running Bear. When the shoeing was completed, Running Bear stepped from the shadows to claim his horse.

"Two dollars," the blacksmith said gruffly.

Running Bear took two silver coins from the

pocket of his cotton shirt. He handed them to the blacksmith and rode away.

Sikwayi watched. He did not understand what the blacksmith had said, but he recognized the coins. That was good pay for so little work. An idea began to form in his mind.

Next a white man led a horse into the shop. Sikwayi shifted his weight from his lame leg. His leg hurt when he stood on it long. It was twisted and shorter than the other leg.

Sikwayi lived alone now. He still ran the trading post, but it was neither so busy nor so prosperous as when his mother had been alive. He could no longer hunt, so he could not go with the other hunters and bargain for their best furs. Without fine furs to trade, his stock of goods had grown smaller.

He had gone back to silversmithing. It was a good trade for a lame man, because he did not have to be away from home long. But he could not get enough work to keep him busy. He had much time to think.

His thinking was mostly about the Cherokees. The white men were driving the Cherokees farther west all the time. They kept taking the Cherokees' lands and homes. Now the Cherokees were beginning to wonder whether the white men would ever stop.

So far the Americans had not taken Etowah. The village was located on a rocky hillside. The soil was poor and crops did not grow well. Even Sikwayi's garden was not so nice as the old one had been. But he did take care of his fruit trees. He loved his orchard.

"If only the Cherokees would join forces and fight back!" he sometimes thought. But every village still seemed to think only of itself.

Some people said the eastern Cherokees should move beyond the Mississippi River. They would be safe there because the white men never would go that far. Perhaps, if they moved, the Cherokees could even find their lost kinsmen, who had disappeared so long ago.

Other Cherokees refused to leave, however. "This is our home," they said. "The Great Spirit gave us this land to use as long as we wanted it. We shall not leave."

Meanwhile, the white men came in ever-increasing numbers. It seemed only a matter of time until they would take all the land of the

119

Cherokees. The Cherokees seemed to be as helpless as the pigeons in the Pigeon Dance.

Sikwayi tried to think of some way to help the Cherokees. But so far he had found none.

The white customer's horse was finally shod. The man came forward to claim it.

"One dollar," said the blacksmith.

Sikwayi watched the white man hand the blacksmith one coin. One coin instead of two!

"Running Bear paid you two coins!" Sikwayi cried in Cherokee.

The blacksmith looked at him, then at the customer. "What's wrong with that Indian? What's he saying?"

The customer shrugged.

"I guess he doesn't know I always charge Indians twice what a job is worth," the blacksmith said with a laugh. "It's easy to beat them out of money."

Sikwayi understood this no better than the

blacksmith's other remark. But he did understand that Running Bear had been cheated. He turned on his heel and limped angrily away.

"I know what I'll do!" he thought. "I'll become a blacksmith! A lot of our people are taking tools and wagon rims and such things to white blacksmiths to have them mended. They're taking their horses to be shod, too. And they probably are being cheated. I'll watch the blacksmith and learn his trade!"

Excitement rose in him. He limped a little faster. "I'll make my own tools and set up shop in the shed beside the cabin."

He hurried home happily. At last he had found a way to help his people.

WHITE MAN'S MAGIC

One day Sikwayi was returning to his home from Tellico. As he passed a small log cabin on the edge of Tellico, he heard a strange babbling sound. Puzzled, he stopped to listen.

"I-n—in, d-i—di, a-n—an, Indian! I-n—in, d-i—di, a-n—an, Indian!"

Indian! That was the white man's name for the red man, just as *u-na-ga* was the Cherokee name for white man. It was one of the few white man's words Sikwayi knew. But what did the other sounds mean?

Quietly Sikwayi walked toward the door of the cabin. He stood in the doorway and watched and listened, as he had watched and listened at the blacksmith shop.

Inside were several rough benches, on which sat a dozen children. Sikwayi knew some of them. There was Allen Jenkins, the blacksmith's son. There was Sarah Hicks, the daughter of his friend, Charley Hicks. Charley Hicks was half Cherokee and half white, too. He lived in Tellico and sent his children to the white man's school.

Charley could look at the scratches on the talking leaves and tell what they said.

"Would you like to come in?" someone asked.

Startled, Sikwayi looked up. The young wife of the white missionary, or preacher, in the village smiled at him. Her name was Mary Adkins, and she was the schoolteacher. The Cherokees liked her and her husband, too.

The Adkinses were two white people who did not want anything from the Cherokees. They spent their time doing things for others. They had taught some of the Cherokees to worship the white man's God. They were fair to everyone.

Sikwayi did not understand what Mrs. Adkins said. But he stepped inside when she waved him toward a bench. She handed him something that he had never seen before. It was a book with white pages in it. The pages were covered with queer marks like those on the talking leaves. The marks were not quite the same, but Sikawyi knew that they must mean the same things. He knew that these pages were talking leaves.

A thrill ran through him. On the stiff back of the book was printed FIRST SCHOOL SPELLER, although Sikwayi didn't know this. He handled the book with awe.

Sikwayi sat on the bench looking at the book. On the first page were twenty-six strange shapes. On the other pages the same shapes reappeared many times over. After puzzling over them for a time, Sikwayi suddenly smiled with under-standing. The way the shapes were arranged with other shapes was the clue to what they said!

He watched the teacher put three shapes on a slate. She held the slate up and smiled at him.

"Would you like to learn, too?" she asked.

Sikwayi nodded, although he was not quite certain what she had said.

Mrs. Adkins pointed to the shapes on the slate. The first one looked like a half moon. "C," she

said as she pointed to it. The next one looked like a pointed tree. "A," she said. The last one looked like a stick with another stick on top. "T," she said. Then she said, "CAT!"

Cat! Sikwayi jumped up in excitement. That meant wesa! He had learned a word of the talking leaves!

The teacher said, "Recess!" The children raced outdoors. Sikwayi rose and handed the book to the teacher.

"You may keep it if you wish," Mrs. Adkins said, returning it.

Sikwayi nodded his thanks. Then, holding the book close, he hurried home. All thoughts of the blacksmith shop were gone. Several times he stopped and drew the three shapes in the dirt.

"Cat!" he said, pleased. "Wesa!"

So that was the white man's magic!

GREAT POWER

Woodpecker, Black Fox, Little Beaver, and two other neighbors stood watching Sikwayi. They watched him stop work on the forge in his shed and pick up the white man's speller. They shook their heads. He put down the book and began to draw something in the dirt with a stick. His friends looked at one another. "Was he under a spell?" their eyes seemed to ask.

"He is making magic," said Rain Crow angrily.

Rain Crow was the shaman, or medicine man, of the town of Etowah.

"It is because he is a cripple," Rain Crow went on. "Cripples have great magic powers. All medicine men know that."

With his lame foot, Sikwayi rubbed out what he had drawn in the dirt. Then he drew something else.

Rain Crow shook his head. "We must keep an eye on him," he whispered. "He may be casting spells on us."

With fear in their hearts, Sikwayi's friends went away.

Ever since Mrs. Adkins had given him the speller, Sikwayi had been thinking about it. He had spent every spare moment studying it. Sometimes he would stop suddenly in the middle of his work and pick up the book. With one finger, he would trace the twenty-six queer little shapes on the first page. With a stick he would copy them in the dirt. Then he would stand and look at them thoughtfully.

He saw that several of the queer shapes would be grouped together at the top of a page in the book. They made words, he was sure. Then these would be strung together at the bottom of the page to put down different thoughts.

Sikwayi copied some of the words. He wondered what they said. He wished that he knew how the shapes were put together to make words.

One afternoon Charley Hicks stopped in the shop. Sikwayi had not seen him for a long time.

"You have a fine blacksmith shop here," Charley said. "It is good that one of our own people has started such a shop."

Sikwayi nodded, pleased.

He showed the speller to Charley and asked him to explain it. Charley sat down. Together he and Sikwayi studied the speller. Charley told Sikwayi the meanings of many of the words.

Sikwayi was delighted to learn more about the white man's talking leaves. He limped around the shop excitedly.

"If only we Cherokees could write like that!" he cried. "If we had talking leaves of our own we could spread the wisdom of the head chiefs of Chota to all the villages. Then we could band together and oppose the white men. Perhaps we could even send messages to the Lost Cherokees, wherever they are. Who knows what we could do if we were all united?"

Charley smiled quietly. "You are a fine silver-smith and a good blacksmith, Sikwayi," he said. "Our people like to trade in your store. Don't neglect business for these new ideas."

Sikwayi didn't answer. He didn't even hear Charley leave. His mind was whirling with many new thoughts.

"If the Cherokee language can be spoken," he thought, "why can't it be written down?"

His leg began to hurt, and he sat down to rest it. "Why do I have to be crippled when there is so much to do?" he wondered. "Still, I have heard that cripples are given great powers. If that is so, good! I shall need them."

He weighed the speller idly in his hand, then looked at the letters on its cover.

"Somehow, someday," he said aloud, "I'm going to think of a way to write Cherokee!"

His Father's Name

ONE morning in 1809 Sikwayi was busy in his workshop beside the trading post. He was engraving a design on a handsome silver breastplate or medallion for his friend, John Ross.

John Ross was a Cherokee. His father, like Sikwayi's, had been a white man. Ross was an important chief in the Cherokee council.

On the breastplate Sikwayi had drawn an eagle, with wings outspread. It was a design he loved. He used it often, changing it a little each time. He was not merely a silversmith now. He had become a fine artist as well. All the people who saw his work said that he was the finest silversmith in the Cherokee nation. It had taken many years for him to become so well known.

Sikwayi was glad that so many people admired his work in silver. He was glad that people brought things to his blacksmith shop to be repaired and that they bought things in his trading post. But one thing made him sad. For all his efforts, he had not discovered a way to write in the Cherokee language.

In one corner of his workshop were stacks of pieces of birchbark. On each piece was a symbol or sign for a Cherokee word. Some of the symbols were the queer shapes from the white man's speller. Others Sikwayi had made up himself. But there were so many words in the Cherokee language that he had finally run out of symbols. And he had made up so many symbols that even he could not remember them all.

Sikwayi's eyes turned from the pile of birchbark back to the breastplate. He had no time

for birchbark now. He must finish the breastplate before John Ross came to get it. He picked
up his engraving tool again.

"Let us burn them," a voice said from the
doorway. "They gather dust."

Sikwayi turned. It was U-ti-yu, his wife.

"Burn what?" he asked.

She nodded toward the pile of bark. "You do
not work on them any longer."

"Leave them alone," Sikwayi said. "I have
not given up. Some day I might need them."

"If you must read and write as the white men do, learn to read and write in the white man's language. Why must you do it in the language of the Cherokees?"

"You do not understand," Sikwayi said patiently. "The Cherokees must have their own talking leaves. Why should I learn the white man's language to send messages to people of my own race?"

"Hah!" U-ti-yu turned abruptly to the door. "Stubborn dreamer!"

She went outside, and Sikwayi could hear their three children calling to her from the orchard. He turned back to his bench.

"Someday," he muttered to himself as he leaned over the breastplate, "someday I shall do it. I know I shall!"

A short time later his cousin and old friend Lone Bear stopped to see him. Lone Bear now lived in the near-by village of Roaring Springs.

After greeting Sikwayi, Lone Bear stood beside him in silence for several minutes, watching him work. Lone Bear marveled at Sikwayi's skill in cutting the delicate lines of the pattern. Each mark was just long enough and heavy enough to have the desired effect.

At last Sikwayi put down his tools and turned to Lone Bear with a smile.

"Well, cousin," he said, "what news do you bring from Roaring Springs?"

"None," Lone Bear replied. "Our crops are good, but hunting is not what it used to be. I have been hunting in the hills above Etowah, but found nothing." He sighed. "Now I must return home empty-handed. It is not good for a people to be without meat."

"Have you no cattle?"

"Not enough for meat." Stepping forward, Lone Bear traced the delicate engraving on the breastplate. The silver gleamed warmly in the afternoon sunlight that fell slanting through the open window.

"I never thought that I would like the life of a silversmith," he went on. "But perhaps after all it is better than mine. At least the white man pays you for what you do. But what can the hunter do when the white man has taken all his land? I was thinking that yesterday when I saw a buckle that you had made."

"A buckle?" Sikwayi lifted his head. "Where?"

"In the white man's trading post at Roaring Springs. The white man said you had made it."

There was a moment of silence. Then Sikwayi said angrily, "I made no buckle for the trader at Roaring Springs! How can he say that when it is not my work?"

"He thought it was your work, cousin. It was sold to him as yours. How would he know?"

Sikwayi sighed. "Yes, how would he know unless I told him? This has happened before.

The other day I saw some pieces in a white man's store in Tellico. The white man said they were mine, but they were not. They were just copies."

"I could not tell the difference between your work and copies," Lone Bear said.

"No, I suppose not. It would be hard if you did not know my work well. But how am I to stop these copies?"

A MAN'S NAME

The two men stood in the doorway of the cabin. One was Charley Hicks. The other was a white man. In one hand the white man carried a large folder. In the other he had a wooden case. On his back was a pack.

"You are Sikwayi, the great Cherokee silversmith?" the white man asked politely.

Sikwayi raised his head. He could not understand what the man said, but he recognized his own name when the man spoke it. He looked questioningly at Charley Hicks.

This man was different from most of the white men Sikwayi had seen. His red beard was trimmed and came to a point at the chin. His features were regular and there was a kindly twinkle in his eyes. His voice was gentle.

"I am Robert Stevens," the white man said, bowing slightly. "I am an artist. I have heard much about you. I should like to paint your portrait if I may."

Charley translated, or changed, his words into Cherokee for Sikwayi.

Sikwayi looked at the man with greater interest. An artist! He had heard of the white men's paintings. They were of people and scenes and animals, and they were hung in buildings and lasted forever. He had often wished that he could see such a painting. Now here was his chance. He smiled at the stranger.

138

"You may do so and welcome," he said.

Mr. Stevens opened his folder. From it he brought a piece of canvas stretched on a frame. He untied the pack and took from it a folding easel. He set up the easel and placed the canvas on it. Then he opened the case. It was filled with colored powders, oils, and brushes. There was a palette on which to mix the paints.

Sikwayi's eyes took in everything that Mr. Stevens did. Soon the artist was ready.

"I should like to paint you at your bench," Mr. Stevens said through Charley. "Perhaps you could be working on the breastplate. I like the way the sun shines through the window above the bench and gleams on the silver."

Sikwayi was surprised when Charley translated this. One of his father's people noticed the beauty around him! Sikwayi was used to white men who thought of nothing but land and more land. Sikwayi liked this white man, Stevens.

Scratch, scratch. Sikwayi could hear the charcoal as Stevens made a quick sketch on the canvas. He wished that he could watch and pose at the same time.

Presently U-ti-yu and the children gathered behind Mr. Stevens.

"It looks like Father already!" cried Ga-li-la-hi, Gentle One, the oldest girl.

Mr. Stevens leaned forward. He squinted at the canvas. He smiled with satisfaction when Charley repeated Gentle One's remark.

"I am happy she thinks so," he said. He cocked his head to one side, studying the sketch again. "Yes," he added, "I think it is ready for paint."

"May I see what you have done?" Sikwayi asked through Charley.

"Of course," said Mr. Stevens. He began to mix oil with some of his colored powders.

Sikwayi stood before the canvas. The sketchy lines formed a surprising likeness of him.

140

"Very good," he said, pleased.

All that day and the next Sikwayi posed at the bench. At last Mr. Stevens was finished.

"Now I shall sign it," Mr. Stevens said. In one corner he put some of the queer shapes that were in Sikwayi's speller.

"What is that?" Sikwayi asked Charley.

"It is his name," said Charley. "He is putting it there so that anyone who looks at the picture will know he painted it."

Sikwayi's eyes opened wide with surprise.

Mr. Stevens started to pack. He stood up. "Tell Sikwayi our silversmiths sign their work, too," he said to Charley.

Sikwayi gazed keenly at Mr. Stevens.

"Perhaps I should sign my work," he said.

Mr. Stevens motioned toward the breastplate. "You should sign that," he laughed. "Any man who can make a thing as beautiful as that should put his name on it."

Sikwayi thought a great deal about what Mr. Stevens had said. He decided to put his own name on the silver things he made. Then no other silversmith could make copies of his work and sell them as his.

But Sikwayi had no sooner decided this than another thought occurred to him. How could he write his name down? It could be spoken in Cherokee, of course, but it could not be written!

"I might use a mark," he told U-ti-yu one day. "Maybe an eagle or a fish. But I would rather use my name, as Mr. Stevens did."

"Go to see your friend Charley Hicks," said U-ti-yu. "Perhaps he can help you."

The next morning Sikwayi started for Tellico. It was a cool but pleasant morning. A mist clung to the hilltops, but the sun soon burned it away and climbed steadily into the blue sky. Birds sang cheerfully in the trees.

143

When he reached Tellico, Sikwayi went straight to the home of Charley Hicks. Charley owned a ferry and a store there.

Charley listened while Sikwayi explained why he had come. Then Charley got a piece of the white man's paper, a quill pen, and some ink and sat down at a table.

"Sikwayi," he murmured aloud. "Si-kwa-yi." He thought for a moment, then tried to put the sounds down in the white man's marks. He read what he had written, shook his head, and drew a line through the letters. "Sikwayi."

Suddenly his eyes lighted up and he wrote quickly. "There! That's it! In my father's tongue your name would be Sequoyah!"

Sequoyah picked up the paper. He looked curiously at the queer shapes that made his name. Then he looked at Charley.

"It is bad that my name can be written in the white man's tongue but not in Cherokee.

144

Charley nodded. "Still, it is so."

For a few moments Sikwayi was silent. Then he said. "Write down my father's name."

Charley looked up in surprise. This was the first time he had ever heard Sequoyah mention his father.

"What was his name?" Charley asked.

Sequoyah thought deeply. He had heard Wurteh speak of his father many times, but the names

of white men sounded queer to him. Then his face brightened.

"Nathaniel!" he said. "That was his name."

After a moment's thought Charley wrote the name down. Sequoyah looked at it curiously.

"What was his other name?" Charley asked. "All white men have two names."

Sequoyah thought again, and finally the name came to him.

"Gist," he said, "Nathaniel Gist. That was my father's name."

Again Charley wrote the word as he thought it sounded. "G-U-E-S-S," he wrote.

Sequoyah looked at the two names. They seemed strange, yet one of them, Guess, was his name, too, his English name. A feeling of pride came over him.

"I could use my father's name on my work," he said thoughtfully. "But Nathaniel would be hard to put down."

"What is it the blacksmith, Jenkins, calls you?" Charley asked. "Not Sequoyah."

"Sometimes he calls me George."

Charley laughed. "George! That's easy. My brother's name is George." He wrote down the name "George Guess."

Sequoyah repeated it. "George Guess. George Guess." Then he nodded his head. "Yes, this would be a good name to put on my work."

He picked up the piece of paper with his new name on it. He folded it and tucked it inside his cotton shirt. Then he thanked Charley and returned to Etowah.

Back in his shop Sikwayi made a die or stamp with the name on it. He heated the die and pressed it into the back of the breastplate.

"GEORGE GUESS," it read.

"Now," he told his wife with a smile, "anyone who sees my work will know who made it."

Useless One

Black Fox left the carcass of a deer before the door of Sequoyah's cabin.

"Here is food for you and your family," he said to U-ti-yu.

Black Fox did not go in. He could no longer respect his friend.

Not long ago Sequoyah had been a fine silversmith and had made beautiful things to sell. He had been a good blacksmith and had shod horses and mended plows and such things for his neighbors. He had bought and sold goods at fair prices in his trading post. He had been a good husband and father.

"Now look at him," Black Fox thought. "His silversmithing bench is covered with dust. His blacksmith shop has been closed for months. There are so few goods in his trading post that hardly anyone goes there any longer. Does Sequoyah care? No! He sits all day and draws queer marks on pieces of bark."

It had happened before, but it was much worse now. Sequoyah walked and acted like someone in a dream. He muttered Cherokee words over and over. Sometimes he went into the woods and sat all day on a log, muttering words to himself. He would get up only long enough to make a mark in the dirt. Then he would sit on his log again and stare into space.

His family would have gone hungry and cold if the neighbors had not helped. U-ti-yu and Tessee, his oldest son, tended the garden and the orchard. Black Fox and other friends provided them with meat.

At first Sequoyah's friends did not mind. But as the months went by they began to grumble. Some became bitter.

"We help his family while he works evil against us," they said. They were sure that he was working on magic spells and signs of some kind that would bring harm to them.

But Sequoyah did not seem to notice what went on around him. He had been like this ever since Charley Hicks had written his English name on paper for him.

Sequoyah had hurried home that day to tell his wife about his talk with Charley. He was full of enthusiasm and determination.

"If my name can be written in English," he said, "it can be written in Cherokee, too."

U-ti-yu threw up her hands. She pointed at the pile of birchbark pieces lying in one corner of the workshop.

"What about these?" she asked. "Do you re-

150

member how long you worked on them? And how far did you get?"

Sequoyah shrugged. "They are no good," he said. "I was not going about it right. You may throw them out now."

U-ti-yu grew angry. "Do you mean you are going through all that again? What about our children? Who is going to feed and clothe them?"

"What I must do, I must do," Sequoyah answered in a soft but determined voice.

He threw away all the old pieces of bark and started over again.

He knew now that he could not use symbols for *words*. There were too many words. He looked again at the white man's alphabet. With twenty-six letters, the white man could write any message he wished to send. Anyone could remember twenty-six little shapes.

Sequoyah sat and thought. He mouthed words of the Cherokee tongue over and over.

Was there some way of writing them down in a smaller number of symbols or shapes?

He thought of his name, Sikwayi. Si-kwa-yi. There were three sounds in it.

Suddenly he sprang to his feet. "I have it! *Sounds!* Why didn't I think of that before?"

The three sounds in his name could be found in many Cherokee words. There were three sounds in his wife's name, too—U-ti-yu. Each sound could be found in many Cherokee words.

"I'll make a symbol for each sound!" he said.

He gathered more pieces of bark and began to make new symbols on them. The longer he worked, the more different sounds he found the Cherokee language had. To find them all was a task that kept him busy for months.

He went over and over all the Cherokee words that he knew or had ever heard. He asked his friends to tell him words. He even stopped strangers and asked them for words.

Then, muttering the words again and again, he separated the sounds. He made a symbol for each sound. Some symbols he made like the letters in the white man's alphabet. Some he changed a little, with a wiggle here or a twist there. Some he made up himself.

The pile of bark pieces in the corner of the cabin grew higher and higher. The dust on his bench grew deeper. His family and home grew shabbier and shabbier.

Sometimes he thought he had set down all the words and sounds there were in the Cherokee language. Then he would discover words with other sounds.

At last he grew discouraged. "Am I getting anywhere?" he wondered. "Have I started another impossible task?"

One day he wandered off into the forest. He fought the whole problem out with himself. When he returned, he cleaned out his shop and started to work at silversmithing again. He opened up his blacksmith shop. Slowly he increased the stock of goods in his trading post.

Dust settled on the pieces of birchbark piled in one corner of the shop.

MAN OF PEACE

Three years passed. In 1812 the English and the Americans went to war. Once again the

English wanted the Cherokees to fight on their side. The Cherokees could not decide. They had fought with the English once and had lost. The Americans had dealt severely with the Cherokees for that. Now the Cherokees wondered.

The head chiefs met to discuss the matter.

"We must always live close to the Americans, whether we want to or not," they said. "Perhaps we should fight on their side this time. If they win again, we may be able to make better treaties with them later on."

The Cherokee people agreed, but they were not eager to go to war. Then came news that the Creeks were fighting on the side of the English. That settled it.

"We will fight with the Americans," the Cherokees said.

The Cherokees and Creeks hated one another. They had been enemies even before the coming of the white men. They had fought over hunting grounds. They had raided one another's villages and destroyed one another's crops for as long as anyone knew.

The Cherokees longed to defeat the Creeks. With the Americans on their side, perhaps this was the Cherokees' chance.

The Americans called for volunteers. Many Cherokees enlisted to fight in the American army.

Sequoyah did not want to go to war. He was a man of peace. But this war was important, perhaps more important than anything else. For a long time he had wanted to help his people, but had failed in everything he had tried. This might be his last chance.

He talked it over with U-ti-yu.

"I can take care of the trading post," she said. "The children can take care of the garden and the cows and sheep. We will get along."

Sequoyah glanced at the pile of birchbark pieces in the corner. How long and hard he had worked on them! He had hoped that his work would help his people, but it hadn't.

The Cherokees' need for talking leaves was greater than ever now. Some Cherokees had moved to what is now Arkansas and were calling themselves the Nation West. There was no way for the two groups to keep in touch.

"Come live with us," the western Cherokees urged. "We have a big free country here. White men will never want this land."

The eastern Cherokees wanted to stay in their old homes. At the same time they thought that the eastern and western Cherokees should be united in some way. Talking leaves would help to unite them, many said. But the Cherokees had no talking leaves.

After talking it over with U-ti-yu, Sequoyah decided to join the American army. Even though he was lame, he could get about well enough to fight the Creeks.

While he was gone, Sequoyah often longed for news from home. He wondered how U-ti-yu and the children were. He wondered whether business in the trading post was still good. He wondered whether his old friend Woodpecker was still alive or not.

Few of the white men heard from home, either, because mail did not reach the army often. But from time to time a messenger would bring messages to General Andrew Jackson, and with him he also brought letters to some of Jackson's men. Sequoyah noticed that these men were always happier after reading their letters. He was sure the letters brought news from home.

One day he and Black Fox were talking about the white man's letters.

"They must be magic," Black Fox said. "How could they do so much if they were not magic?"

Sequoyah laughed and shook his head. "No, the white man's talking leaves are not really magic," he said. "They are just marks on paper. I could do the same myself. You have seen me do it. But they are just as good as magic."

Still Black Fox was not convinced. He was sure that the talking leaves contained some strange and powerful magic.

The Cherokees fought bravely during the war. At the battle of Horseshoe Bend, on the Tallapoosa River in Alabama, they helped to defeat the Creeks. After this battle, the war was over as far as the Cherokees were concerned. Most of them went home.

On the way home Sequoyah made a decision.

"When I get home I am going to start working on my symbols again," he said. "I still think the Cherokee language can be written down."

A look of concern crossed Black Fox's face. He had hoped his friend had forgotten that nonsense. He stole a look at Sequoyah. His heart sank. His friend was lost in dreams again!

Sequoyah neared his cabin. Happiness rose in his heart. It was spring. All around him fresh green things were growing. The peach and apple trees were in bloom. He sniffed their fragrance. His heart sang with joy. It was good to be home again.

Slowly he rode up to the cabin. His eyes missed nothing. Smoke was curling from the chimney. The smell of cooking food came to him.

His daughter, Ga-li-la-hi, came to the door. She looked out and saw Sequoyah.

"Father!" she cried happily and ran to him.

Soon he was surrounded by all the members of his family. After his welcome, he walked around his little farm. Everything was in good shape. With the help of the children, U-ti-yu had done well. Only his silversmithing bench and his blacksmith shop were idle.

"When I work on my birchbark pieces again,"

he thought, "I will not neglect everything else. I will make some silver pieces. I will take care of the blacksmith shop. I will help U-ti-yu in the trading post. After all, much of my work is done. It is all set down on the pieces of bark in the corner."

He was happy and content. He went into the cabin for the noonday meal.

"This is the best meal I have had since I left home," he said as he sat at the rough-hewn table. There were bowls of stew and cooked dried beans before him. There were cornbread, butter, and plenty of milk.

"I killed a turkey yesterday," his son Tessee said proudly. He was big for his age. He handled a rifle with skill.

"You are a good provider, my son," Sequoyah said with a smile.

U-ti-yu smiled with pleasure.

After eating, Sequoyah went to his shop. He

glanced first at the corner near the fireplace. His face froze with horror.

"My pieces of bark!" he cried. "What has become of them?"

"Oh, those?" said U-ti-yu lightly. "I burned them a few months ago."

Sequoyah stared in astonishment. *"You— burned—them?"*

"Yes. They weren't any good."

Sequoyah turned away blindly. Suddenly his happiness had changed to despair. All the way home he had been thinking about those pieces of birchbark. Now they were gone!

Without a word he left the shop and went off to the forest, alone. For hours he wandered about, thinking. Night had come by the time he returned home. But his anger and sorrow were gone, and he was peaceful at heart. He had come to a decision in the forest. Tomorrow morning he would start over again!

A Bag of Gold

ONE morning in 1821 Sequoyah stood in the doorway of his new home in Arkansas. The sun was above the eastern hills. Leaves rustled cheerfully in the summer breeze. There was a smell of flowers and moist earth in the air.

Sequoyah was happy this morning. Many things had happened since he had left the army in 1815. But all of the things that had happened faded away to nothing today. They had not been important. The really important things were starting just now.

"Sequoyah." His second wife, Sally, came to stand at his side. "Are you hungry?"

"Very hungry," he said with a smile. "We'll eat and then we'll go." He stepped into the yard. "Ah-yo-ka! Come! It is time to eat."

At once a small girl came running from the apple orchard behind the cabin. Her eyes were bright with eagerness. "Will we go, Father?" she cried. "After we have eaten?"

Sequoyah laughed and held her close. "Yes, my little one. After we have eaten. And are you still eager to go? You do not wish to stay home with your mother and brother and sister?"

"Oh, no, Father!" Ah-yo-ka cried. "I would like to go with you."

"Good! Then run inside and eat."

Sequoyah paused to take a last look at the farm. Then, with a smile, he turned and entered the cabin himself.

He was happier this morning than he had been at any time for years. At last, after years of struggle and disappointing failure, he had completed his alphabet. He had actually worked out a way to write the Cherokee language. Not only that, he had taught his daughter, Ah-yo-ka, to read and write as well.

Working out the alphabet had been a greater task than he had thought it would be. But he had finished it. And now he would take the alphabet to the Cherokee Tribal Council at New Echota. New Echota was now the capital of the Cherokee nation. It was located in Georgia.

After his return from the war, Sequoyah had gone to work on the alphabet again. He remembered some of the characters, but many he had forgotten. As a result, he had had to start almost from the beginning again.

He had promised himself that he would attend to business first. But he was soon spending most of his time on the alphabet, as he had done before. He could not help it.

At first the neighbors laughed. When they

brought their horses to be shod, they would find Sequoyah making strange marks on pieces of bark. When they came to the trading post, one of the children would have to wait on them. Sequoyah would be sitting in a corner working on his symbols and would not even notice that the customers were there.

Before long, however, the neighbors' laughter turned to scorn.

"Tessee is more of a man than his father," they said. "At least he goes hunting to put meat on the table. Sequoyah sits in a corner all day like a child, playing with pieces of bark."

Then the neighbors grew fearful.

"Sequoyah is of the Red Paint clan," they whispered among themselves. "The people of that clan have always been powerful wizards. He is a cripple, too, and cripples have magic powers."

"Perhaps he will cast a spell on us!" someone said fearfully.

"He is to blame for all the troubles we have been having," another said.

"Yes!" cried still another. "His spells have helped the white man take our land."

Silence greeted this remark. Then someone said slowly, "It is true. Since Sequoyah started making these strange marks, we have lost much land. Sequoyah *must* be to blame!"

The talk spread, and before long Sequoyah and his family were outcasts. It made Sequoyah sad that his people could not see that he was trying to help them.

But he was sure now that he was on the right track, and he would not give up. He had reduced the number of symbols to a hundred, and he hoped to reduce it still more. He decided to leave home and move to Arkansas. Perhaps the western Cherokees would be more understanding.

When he suggested this to U-ti-yu, she became angry. "Leave my home and family and friends?

I will not! Not for a man whose foolish dreams keep him from supporting his family!"

Sequoyah sighed and went for a walk in the woods. He knew that U-ti-yu was right. He should work in the blacksmith shop more often. He should make more valuable things in silver. He also should help in the trading post.

But sometimes there were things that a man had to do, even when they seemed to be wrong. Completing his alphabet was one of them. He was sorry that he was being unfair to U-ti-yu and the children. But the power to read and write, the power to have talking leaves of their own, would help the whole Cherokee Nation. It would help the Cherokees fight against the white man's steady conquest of their land.

It was the whole nation, and not just his family, that Sequoyah was working for. He knew that if he kept on working he would finally reach his goal.

When he returned home, nothing more was said about his plan to go to Arkansas. He still wanted to go, but he dreaded raising the question again. U-ti-yu said nothing, and life went on as before, unhappily.

Then U-ti-yu suddenly fell ill and died. After the burial, Sequoyah gathered his children together in the cabin.

"Life is not good here now," he said. "The white men take more of our land each year. Soon they will try to drive us out entirely. I am going west to the land where our relatives, the western Cherokees, live. You older ones, Tessee and Ga-li-la-hi, are old enough to decide for yourselves. You may stay here with your friends or you may go with me. I shall take the baby, Ah-yo-ka, with me."

Both Tessee and Ga-li-la-hi decided to stay. Sequoyah left them what he had. When he set out for the west, he took only a little food and

170

some clothes for himself and Ah-yo-ka. He took his rifle and, most important of all, a deerskin with his symbols painted on it.

That had been three years ago. Since then he had married Sally and worked hard on his farm. Ah-yo-ka was now six.

But most important of all to Sequoyah, he had finished his alphabet. With the help of Sally and

Ah-yo-ka, he had cut the number of symbols to eighty-six. Ah-yo-ka learned to read and write as well as he. And now the two of them were going to New Echota to show his alphabet to the Tribal Council.

NEW ECHOTA

Sequoyah's friend John Ross was the chairman of the Tribal Council. He had a big house in New Echota, in which he lived when the Council was meeting. As soon as they reached New Echota, Sequoyah and Ah-yo-ka went to see him.

Sequoyah told Ross about his alphabet. Ross listened solemnly. Then he rose and paced up and down the room.

"If what you say is true," he said, "you have done something no one man has ever done before. You have invented a way by which a spoken language can be written and read."

172

Sequoyah shook his head. "I do not know about that," he said. "I only know what I can do with my alphabet. I can teach anyone who can speak Cherokee to read and write it."

Ross nodded at Ah-yo-ka. "You say you have taught Ah-yo-ka to do this?" He was still a little doubtful.

Sequoyah looked fondly at his daughter. She sat in a straight-backed chair, swinging her feet. She looked very small and young.

"She learned it in three days," he said proudly. Then he added quickly, "Of course, she had heard me talking about it for a long time. It might take other people a week or more."

John Ross smiled.

"That is still a very short time," he said. "It takes white children years to learn to read and write the English language."

Sequoyah leaned back. He shrugged. "That may be so," he said. "But what I say about Ah-

173

yo-ka is true. I should like to show the Council. If they will use my alphabet, the Cherokees can have talking leaves, too."

John Ross went on pacing back and forth. His brows met in a thoughtful frown.

"If what you say is true," he murmured, "we can have our own schools. We can have our own books and newspapers. We can set down our laws for everyone to read. We can write down our history, our own stories and songs. Such things should not be forgotten."

Sequoyah nodded. He leaned forward.

"And we can send messages to one another," he said earnestly. "You eastern Cherokees can join forces with the western Cherokees. We can become stronger by doing this."

John Ross's excitement rose.

"You and your daughter come to the Council House early tomorrow morning," he said. "I will call the chiefs together."

174

"Thank you," Sequoyah said. He rose to leave.

"Where are you staying?" Ross asked.

"We will sleep in the woods outside the town," Sequoyah said.

"No, you won't," Ross laughed. "You will stay overnight with us."

John Ross was a wealthy and educated man. He was more white than Indian. He was the most important man in the Cherokee nation. Sequoyah was pleased because Ross had not laughed at him.

That evening, after they had eaten, Sequoyah and Ah-yo-ka went for a walk.

"This town is quite different from the Chota near which I lived," he told Ah-yo-ka. "It is more like a white man's town than an Indian town."

There were straight streets, with several stores and a gristmill. The Council House was a big two-storied building. There were a church and a school and many log cabins. Some of the better homes and buildings were made of brick. New Echota was called the capital of the Cherokee nation.

Sequoyah did not sleep much that night. He kept thinking about tomorrow, and worrying. He had only told John Ross that Ah-yo-ka could read and write in Cherokee. He had not shown him. Would she do as he had said she would?

He had worked hard for a long time to perfect his alphabet. He had failed often in the past. Would he fail again tomorrow?

TEACH US

Ah-yo-ka stood before all the chiefs of the Cherokees. She was trembling inside, but she did not show it.

Sequoyah was proud of his little daughter. He knew how she felt, because he was trembling inside himself.

He had heard some of the chiefs talking as he came into the Council House.

"Sequoyah is a wizard, a magician!" one of them said. "He has been making evil magic for the Cherokees for many years."

"All our troubles with the white men can be laid to him," growled another.

"He should be driven from the nation!" cried a third chief.

"He is a no-good dreamer."

"He boasts of doing something no man could have done alone."

"Read and write in Cherokee! Ha! Does he think the Little People have taken our wits, along with his?"

So the chiefs had talked as they filed into the council room. They had been surprised on seeing Ah-yo-ka there. Her hair hung in two neat braids. Her bright cotton dress was clean and starched. John Ross's wife had seen to that.

"Sequoyah would bring disgrace on his daughter, too?" the chiefs asked one another.

They had flung angry glances at Sequoyah and passed by him without speaking.

Their angry looks hurt Sequoyah as much as those of his old neighbors had. As he stood waiting and watching, he wondered whether he would be able to change those angry looks to smiles of friendship today.

So much depended on Ah-yo-ka, he knew. She was a bright child. She could do all that he claimed she could. But would she become frightened before these stern men? Would she forget what she had learned?

"Let us proceed," John Ross said finally from the head of the council table. He turned to Sequoyah. "You wish to show us how to read and write in Cherokee. How will you do this?"

Sequoyah took a deep breath.

"I will leave the room," he said quietly. "Any

one of you can give my daughter a message. She will write it down on this piece of paper. When I come in, I will read it."

Laughter rippled around the room. The air almost crackled with the chiefs' scorn.

John Ross did not laugh. He nodded. Sequoyah limped from the room. Ross carefully shut the door behind him. Then he turned to speak to the chiefs.

"Now," he said in a low voice, "will one of you give the little girl a message?"

One chief rose.

"I will," he said. He turned to Ah-yo-ka. "The Lame One is a fool."

Red spots burned on Ah-yo-ka's cheeks. But she said nothing. She made some strange marks on the piece of paper. John Ross went to the door. He opened it and motioned Sequoyah inside.

Sequoyah picked up the piece of paper. His

face flushed, too. His lips formed a thin line. But he was happy inside. Ah-yo-ka had forgotten nothing. The marks on the paper were as easy to follow as the path of a bear in snow.

"The Lame One is a fool," he said.

A surprised murmur went around the room.

"It is a trick!" cried the one who had given the message. "He listened at the door."

"We will try again," said another. "This time Sequoyah must go outside and sit under a tree. Then we can see him through the window."

Sequoyah went outside. He sat under a tree. The chiefs could see him. One of them gave Ah-yo-ka another message, a longer one. She set it down on paper. Sequoyah came back and read it, word for word.

The chiefs sat spellbound. They tried again and again to trip Sequoyah and Ah-yo-ka. But they could not.

They sent Ah-yo-ka outside. They gave messages to Sequoyah. He wrote them down and gave them to Ah-yo-ka when she returned to the room. She read them easily in her clear, high voice. She smiled happily.

At last a cheer went up.

"He has given every Cherokee something worth more than a bag of gold!" one chief cried.

"Teach us!" cried the others. "Teach us to read and write in Cherokee!"

Days of Honor

THE OLD man sat in the sunlight, smoking his pipe. Summer had come to Indian Territory, bringing warm weather and green leaves and grass. Somewhere a bird was singing. Behind the cabin the old man could hear his son and grandson talking as they worked in the fields.

The old man closed his eyes and leaned back in his chair. He was glad that summer had come again. Now he could get ready to leave.

For a long time he had been planning a journey. There was a legend among the Cherokees that one of their tribes had gone to Mexico. The old man wanted to follow that tribe.

First of all, he wanted to know whether the legend was true. But even more important, he wanted to visit the Indian tribes in the Southwest and in Mexico. He wanted to learn whether their languages could be written in the Cherokee alphabet. If they could, then these tribes, too, could learn to read and write without having to learn the white man's tongue.

Presently the old man heard the sound of horses' hoofs and opened his eyes. Two strange men were riding up the lane to the cabin. Both were Cherokees, but they were wearing white men's clothes. As they drew near, the old man rose to his feet.

A door behind him opened and a woman came to stand at his side.

"Who are they?" she asked. "Do you know them, Sequoyah?"

"No, Sally," he said. "They have probably just stopped to visit."

184

Many people came to visit Sequoyah now, for he was famous throughout the Cherokee nation. Forgotten were the days when he was considered a dangerous wizard. Forgotten, too, were the days when he was laughed at as a lazy and worthless dreamer.

Now everyone admitted that his invention of an alphabet was one of the Cherokee's greatest gifts. It had made them the most highly educated and civilized Indians in North America. They had their own schools, their own books, and their own newspaper. All these things had been made possible by Sequoyah's alphabet.

"Welcome!" Sequoyah called as the two strangers stopped in front of the house.

"Have we the honor of addressing Sequoyah?" asked one of the men.

Sequoyah nodded. "I am he."

"Good!" said the other. "We bring you a message from the Cherokee National Council."

"Come up, come up," Sequoyah cried. "I am glad to hear from my old friend John Ross and the other chiefs. It has been a long time since I attended a meeting of the Council."

"And the nation misses you, Sequoyah," the older man said. "I can remember seeing you at the Council meetings and being told who you were. I can even remember when you came to my home in Tellico long ago. You and your daughter were teaching the eastern Cherokees to read and write in your alphabet."

"Tellico!" Sequoyah sighed, remembering. "That *was* a long time ago. The little girl is a mother now, and her father is an old man. How many things have happened since those days!"

They all fell silent as they thought of the difficult and unhappy times the Cherokees had known. Then Sequoyah murmured, "Tellico!" and shook his head again.

"We visited many towns in those days, Ah-yo-ka and I," he went on. "Wherever we went, word had gone ahead that the Council had adopted my alphabet. And everywhere people were eager to learn. Even in Tellico, where my old neighbors had laughed at me.

"Then the Council sent us back here to teach the western Cherokees, and people were just as eager here. In no time at all letters were going back and forth between the eastern Cherokees and the western Cherokees."

"Your alphabet did more than anything else to join the two parts of our nation together," said the older messenger.

"Perhaps, perhaps," Sequoyah said. "It makes me happy to think so. I always wanted to do something to unite our people."

"I was too young to remember those days," the younger messenger said. "But I can remember when the first newspaper was published. It was in 1830, wasn't it?"

Sequoyah shook his head with a smile. "February 21, 1828. I was not in New Echota at the time, but I heard about it later from friends. The type was made in Boston, and the paper came from Knoxville. 'The Cherokee Phoenix,' that newspaper was called. And it was ours, too, partly printed in our own alphabet."

He sank down in his chair and fingered the silver medal that hung on a chain around his neck. The medal had been given to him by the National Council. On one side were two crossed pipes, the ancient Indian symbols of law and religion. On the other side was a man's head and an inscription written in English and Cherokee.

"Presented to George Guess," read the inscription, "by the General Council of the Cherokee Nation, for his ingenuity in the invention of the Cherokee alphabet."

"You have a message?" Sequoyah asked.

"Our business will not take long," the older

messenger said. "You remember that two years ago the Council voted you an allowance."

Sequoyah nodded.

"The Council has now voted to change that allowance. Here is their message." He handed Sequoyah a piece of paper.

Sequoyah opened the paper and read. "The allowance we voted to Sequoyah will now be changed to an annuity of three hundred dollars, to be paid to him each year so long as he shall live, and to his widow."

As he read the words, Sequoyah smiled happily. Three hundred dollars a year would be more than enough to live on. Now the last problem about his trip to Mexico was solved. He would not have to worry about Sally while he was gone.

"Thank you, my friends," he said. "I hope you will spend the night with us. I would like to hear about my old friends. I do not see many people these days."

"Things have changed," the older messenger said sadly. "Ever since the white men drove the eastern Cherokees out of their homes, life has been hard. I don't like this Indian Territory to which they have sent us."

"I know," Sequoyah said, nodding his head. "I still miss the wooded hills of home, and the cold mountain streams, and the game. But I suppose things have changed there, too."

"Those must have been sad days when the

government ordered you eastern tribes to leave your homes," Sally said.

"Sad indeed," answered the older messenger. "So many of our women and children and older folks died on the way. Each day was a day of tears and sorrow."

"It was truly a Trail of Tears," Sally said. "Why must white men be so hungry for land?"

The messenger shook his head. "Who knows? Who understands the mind of the white man? I think if it had not been for your husband the white men would have destroyed our nation then. Don't you think so, Sequoyah?"

"Who knows?" Sequoyah said. "Perhaps if I had not invented an alphabet someone else would have. There was nothing magic about it, you know. Anyone could have done it."

He smiled suddenly. "Ah, here comes my son, Tessee. Tessee and I are leaving on a long journey to Mexico soon."

The younger man looked surprised, and Se-quoyah laughed heartily.

"Yes, at my age, young man, I'm going to Mexico! I think there is much to learn about our people there. You know, there is an old legend that much of our learning came from Mexico. I want to go there to learn——"

To learn! Always to learn, to understand! That had always been his goal.

The old man talked on, through the evening meal and far into the night, eagerly and excitingly. Sally smiled knowingly as she saw the looks of wonder and fascination on the faces of his listeners.

"Perhaps his body is the body of an old man," she thought. "But his thoughts are the thoughts of a young man, still eager and quick. He will always be like that, I think, guiding his people into the future."

Childhood

OF FAMOUS AMERICANS

CHILDHOOD
OF FAMOUS
AMERICANS

COLONIAL DAYS

JAMES OGLETHORPE, *Parks*
MYLES STANDISH, *Stevenson*
PETER STUYVESANT, *Widdemer*
POCAHONTAS, *Seymour*
VIRGINIA DARE, *Stevenson*
WILLIAM BRADFORD, *Smith*
WILLIAM PENN, *Mason*

STRUGGLE for INDEPENDENCE

ANTHONY WAYNE, *Stevenson*
BEN FRANKLIN, *Stevenson*
BETSY ROSS, *Weil*
DAN MORGAN, *Bryant*
ETHAN ALLEN, *Winders*
FRANCIS MARION, *Steele*
GEORGE ROGERS CLARK, *Wilkie*
GEORGE WASHINGTON, *Stevenson*
ISRAEL PUTNAM, *Stevenson*
JOHN PAUL JONES, *Snow*
JOHN SEVIER, *Steele*
MARTHA WASHINGTON, *Wagoner*
MOLLY PITCHER, *Stevenson*

NATHAN HALE, *Stevenson*
NATHANAEL GREENE, *Peckham*
PAUL REVERE, *Stevenson*
TOM JEFFERSON, *Monsell*

EARLY NATIONAL GROWTH

ABIGAIL ADAMS, *Wagoner*
ALEC HAMILTON, *Higgins*
ANDY JACKSON, *Stevenson*
DAN WEBSTER, *Smith*
DOLLY MADISON, *Monsell*
ELI WHITNEY, *Snow*
HENRY CLAY, *Monsell*
JAMES FENIMORE COOPER, *Winders*
JAMES MONROE, *Widdemer*
JOHN AUDUBON, *Mason*
JOHN MARSHALL, *Monsell*
JOHN QUINCY ADAMS, *Weil*
LUCRETIA MOTT, *Burnett*
MATTHEW CALBRAITH PERRY, *Scharbach*
NANCY HANKS, *Stevenson*
OLIVER HAZARD PERRY, *Long*
RACHEL JACKSON, *Govan*
ROBERT FULTON, *Henry*
SAMUEL MORSE, *Snow*
STEPHEN DECATUR, *Smith*
STEPHEN FOSTER, *Higgins*
WASHINGTON IRVING, *Widdemer*
ZACK TAYLOR, *Wilkie*